Geological Survey of Finland, Special Paper 22

# Geological information for environmental and land-use planning in the Mid-Norden region

edited by Peer-Richard Neeb

Geological Survey of Finland
Espoo 1996

**Neeb, Peer-Richard (ed.) 1996**. Geological information for environmental and land-use planning in the Mid-Norden region. *Geological Survey of Finland, Special Paper 22,* 110 pages, 78 figures, 7 tables.

The present contribution reports the results of the Mid-Norden Sub-Project for environmental geology. The focus of the project has been to compile and prepare geological data stored in the archives of the Geological Surveys of the three member countries. The participants have emphasised different sides of the topic, as will be evident from the national reports.

The Finnish group has produced by GIS a new type of thematic map compiled in a research and development project in the Finnish Geological Survey in cooperation with the planning and environmental authorities of the research area (Iisalmi), demonstrating that geological data stored at GSF can be applied in various ways in urban planning.

The Norwegian report focuses on the application of digital information technology. Information available on printed and manuscript maps has been transformed into a geographical information system (GIS), the suitability of which has been tested at a single municipality (Inderøy). This has demonstrated how geological information is instrumental in producing an overview of the natural resources of a municipality, and, when combined with land-use data from the local planning office, that it will ease the documentation of land-use changes in the area.

In Sweden, different types of environmental geological maps were selected from existing information in for example Skellefteå and Sollefteå. Resource maps, exploitation, risk maps and conflict maps as well as thematic maps for groundwater protection, permeability, vulnerability to acidification, radon potential, landslide risk, heavy metals in water and till and geological monuments have been made available at small scales.

The overall objective of the report is to demonstrate how important the utilisation of geological information can be to the modern planning process and how the Geological Surveys play a vital role in this work.

Key words (GeoRef Thesaurus, AGI): geologic maps, numerical maps, thematic maps, mineral resources, water supply, environmental geology, land use, planning, Finland, Norway, Sweden

*Peer-Richard Neeb, Geological Survey of Norway*
*Box 3006 - Lade, 7002 Trondheim*
*NORWAY*

*E-mail: peer-richard.neeb@ngu.no*

ISBN 951-690-670-2
ISSN 0782-8535

# CONTENTS

# INTRODUCTION

The geological environment is influenced both by natural changes and human impact.

The term environmental geology describes the study of the interaction between human activity and the geological environment. Environmental geology is based on geological knowledge of the natural resources and risks and is a part of the foundation for good management of the environment and resources.

The Mid-Norden Sub-Project for Environmental Geology started in 1988, with the goal of providing basic geological material primarily for use by the environmental and natural resource sectors in physical planning. Within these sectors, the use of geological knowledge in planning has markedly increased in importance during recent years.

The Geological Surveys of Finland (GSF), Sweden (SGU) and Norway (NGU) possess substantial geological data, such as digital maps of bedrock, surface deposits and groundwater, an aerogeophysics registry and various databases. The users seldom employ the geological information directly but instead require an answer to a particular question or problem in physical planning. Hence, the Geological Surveys have produced thematic geological maps to illustrate the methods which have been found to be suitable for a number of planning situations in various geological environments. When producing thematic maps, the Geological Surveys have used GIS (geographical information system) to search through and analyse all the information in their databases.

In this publication, new thematic maps have been developed by geologists in close co-operation with land-use planners in the Mid-Norden area. The goal of this publication has been to increase the use and usefulness of geological information in municipal land-use planning and environmental protection in Finland, Norway and Sweden. The publication describes at least one case history for each country, and the target area embraces the municipalities and counties in the Mid-Norden region (Fig 1).

## General objectives: the environment of the Mid-Norden region

The Mid-Norden Project has taken place in the period 1988–1996 and can be regarded as a direct continuation of the Nord-Kalott Project, from 1980–1986. The Mid-Norden Project dealt with the area from 66° N to 62°45' N (i.e., from Mosjøen–Uddjaure–Kemi in the north to about Ålesund–Sundsvall–Saarijärvi in the south). The project has aimed to provide basic geological material for use primarily in the environmental and natural resource whether when prospecting for ores and industrial minerals, or in physical planning, agriculture and forestry, as well as in medical geology contexts. Within these sectors, geological knowledge has become of greatly increased importance during recent years. Since environmental concerns have increased,this project also included an environmental geology section which illustrated the importance of using geological data in environmental and projecting work and which was based on existing geological material or material produced within the framework of the Mid-Norden Project.

All results from the Mid-Norden Project will be available as printed maps with descriptions and digital datasets on a CD-ROM.

The natural environment may be regarded as the sum of interaction between geology, biology and meteorology that characterise the relationship between life and the planet Earth.

To understand the environmental conditions in the Mid-Norden region it is necessary to to take a closer look at the following physical factors.

* its sub-polar and coastal location which governs its climatic conditions

* its geological history, which clearly separates all the old bedrock (for example, gneisses and granites) from the Quaternary glacial and post-glacial deposits.

* the physical and chemical composition and quality of the geological material.

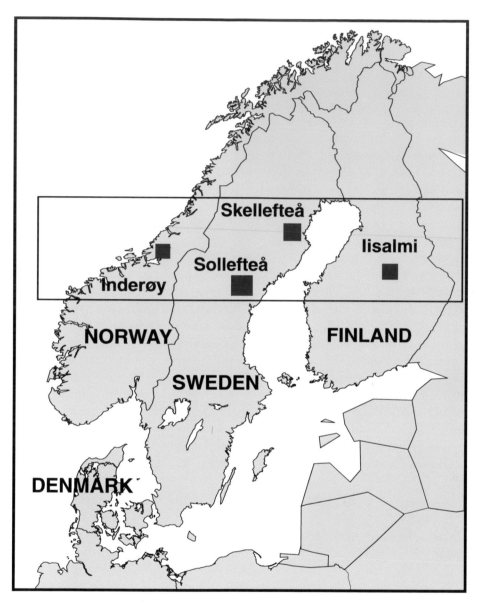

Fig. 1. The target area of this publication in the Mid-Norden region.

## Climatic conditions

Climatic conditions in the Mid-Norden region are influenced by its location between latitudes 62° and 66° North and longitudes 5° and 32° East which produces cool and wet summers and relatively mild and windy winters in the coastal western areas, and warmer summers and relatively cold winters in the continental central and eastern areas. These climatic conditions have an important impact on geological surface processes.

**The geological history**

The geological history is complex and begins with the formation of the great Fennoscandian Shield of ancient crystalline rocks (Precambrian) older than 600 million years. The western part of this shield area was involved in the Caledonian mountain-building cycle (600–350 million years), and then by Rift tectonics with the formation of the Oslo Graben. Younger bedrock (Palaeozoic–Tertiary) is rare on the continent but dominates the off-shore geology. This crystalline basement was subjected to considerable erosion particularly during the Tertiary and Quaternary and during the latter a considerable drift-cover of glacial and fluvio-glacial sediments (gravel, sand and clay) was deposited during and after a number of glaciations.

During the Quaternary period, the old bedrock surface was polished and shaped by the glaciers to form a solid sub-surface under the glacial and post-glacial deposits. This has created a geological situation in the Mid-Norden region which is quite different from those in more southern latitudes and forms a very special base for the study of the environmental geology.

**The physical and chemical composition and quality of the geological materials**

As geological materials like rocks and soils form the basis for all biotic activity on Earth, detailed knowledge of the composition and quality of rocks is very important for planning and managing the environment. The following fields of planning need geoscienctific information and advice:

* Materials and energy (metallic ores, industrial minerals, sand, gravel and rocks suitable for aggregates, etc.,fossil and radioactive fuels)

* Groundwater (aquifers in Quaternary deposits and bedrock)

* Geochemical properties (elements necessary or hazardous for plant, animal and human life as well as resistance to acidification)

* Mechanical properties (geotechnical conditions in the surface and subsurface)

* Waste disposal (infiltration capability, geological barriers against aqueous infiltration from landfill, safe underground storage of toxic and hazardous waste)

* Risks (slope instability, radon gas emission, water erosion, flooding, volcanic activity, earthquake-prone areas, etc.)

* Environmental protection (protection of natural resources, geological and landscape conservation, geo-indicators for monitoring the health of the Earth's surface)

Since the Geological Surveys of Finland, Sweden and Norway were founded more than a century ago, they have collected comprehensive reference material over a wide spectrum of the geological topics. This material includes data on rocks, Surficial deposits, fossils and organic material, geochemistry, geophysics measurements of radioactive radiation, etc. SGU, NGU and GSF thus have a unique reference material in databases for studies of most aspects, environmental change.

**Target readers and the organisation of the publication**

Traditionally, a geoscientist writes for his own colleagues using a number of technical terms and referring to scientific theories that are unfamiliar to planners, politicians and other citizens who do not have a geoscientific training. The target of this publication is, however, this kind of more general reader, and thus it was decided to produce this presentation with a minimum of technical terms, and focusing on matters that have a bearing on the planners problems.

The purpose of this volume will be to focus on problems that are crucial to persons bearing the responsibility for planning and management of the sustainability of the environment and the natural resources. These include the following groups of readers, in order of priority:

* **Planners** who need detailed knowledge of the physical environment and methodologies for assessing opportunities for, and limitations on, land use.

* **Politicians** who need to understand the background for making decisions affecting the environment, which will reinforce their ability to meet the increasing demands of their constituents, and allow them to build a long-term approach to a sustainable future.

* **Business people** who need to understand the increasing impact of environmental factors on business decisions and of economic opportunities in environmental protection and reclamation.

* **Students** who will start challenging careers in a rapidly growing field of great importance to society.

* **Citizens** who want an insight into the physical setting, causes and effects of natural processes and human activities, which will improve their ability to contribute to environmental awareness and stewardship.


## The organisation of the publication

The publication is organised so that the areas in each country are described in three separate papers. The emphasis of each paper is slightly different depending on the local situation and the studies that were most important to the participants in each country.

The areas selected for the preparation of topics on environmental geology are the municipality of Iisalmi in eastern Finland, the municipalities of Skellefteå and Sollefteå in Sweden, and the municipality of Inderøy in Nord-Trøndelag county in Norway.

In Finland, Iisalmi was selected because of the relatively large amount of geological information already available on the area. Natural resources, water supply, susceptibility to acidification, infiltration, soil permeability and environmental impact are all presented on maps in a scale of 1:50,000.

In Sweden, different types of environmental maps were selected based mainly on existing geological information from the Skellefteå and Sollefteå districts in the Mid-Norden region. Some maps have also been extended to cover the entire Mid-Norden region in Sweden. Resource maps, exploitation maps, risk maps and conflict maps are all available in small scales. The same is true of thematic maps for groundwater protection, permeability, vulnerability to acidification, radon potential, land risks, heavy metals in till, geological objects of national interest and conflict maps.

In Norway, the municipality of Inderøy in Nord-Trøndelag county was selected because of the large amount of geological information available. It represents the inner part of the western coastal flank of the Mid-Norden region. Digital datasets of natural resources, groundwater, infiltration, quick clay areas, susceptibility to acidification and land-use conflict maps are derived from traditional geological maps. This area provides a case-study for the direct use of digital data in planning, rather than a reliance on paper copies of maps. This particular study emphases the flexibility of employing digital data not least for planning up-dates.

It is our goal that, in time, every county and local authority that decides to use a digital planning system will be able to carry out their land-use and resource management with relevant geological information available to them in digital form. When this becomes a reality, we will have lived up to our motto to provide "Geology for society".

It is hoped that the Mid-Norden project will be succeeded by a South-Norden project where the ideas and methodologies to use digital geological data in addressing planning and environmental issues will be continued and improved. It is hoped to arrive at a standardisation of such data between the geological surveys involved so that environmental issues can be tackled in a truly multinational manner.


Peer-Richard Neeb

*Geological Survey of Norway*

Geological information for environmental and land-use planning
in the Mid-Norden region
Edited by Peer-Richard Neeb
Geological Survey of Finland, Special Paper 22, 9–37, 1996.

# GEOLOGICAL INFORMATION
# FOR ENVIRONMENTAL AND LAND-USE PLANNING

## Thematic maps of Iisalmi, Finland

Edited by
Maria Nikkarinen

**Nikkarinen, Maria (ed.) 1996.** Geological information for environmental and land-use planning. Thematic maps of Iisalmi, Finland. *Geological Survey of Finland, Special Paper 22*, 9–37, 14 figures, 4 tables.

The Geological Survey of Finland (GSF) holds substantial information on geological data, such as digital maps of bedrock, superficial deposits, groundwater, an aerogeophysics register and various databases. The customer, however, seldom uses the geological information as such but wants a straightforward answer to a particular question, interpreted by an expert. Hence, the GSF endeavours to process the information into thematic maps to meet the current needs of each customer. When producing thematic maps, the GSF uses a GIS to search through and analyse all the information stored in its databases. The accuracy of the interpretation depends on the scale of the source material.

The objective of this project was to produce useful maps of geological data in a simple and lucid form for municipal planning. The usability of the geological mapping data for the production of a new type of thematic map was tested. The maps were compiled as a research and development project of the GSF in collaboration with the planner and the environmental authority of Iisalmi. Iisalmi was selected as a pilot area for the municipal thematic maps, partly because of the fairly high coverage of geological information already available on the area.

The thematic maps of natural resources, water supply, acidification susceptibility and environmental impact are examples of the application of geological information. This contribution contains extracts from thematic maps, descriptions of the source data used for producing the maps and in-depth information on the use of the maps. Grounds for the interpretations are given and the applications of the maps are discussed. The project showed that the GSF has a wealth of data on soil properties that can be applied in various ways in urban planning. The use of geological information in such planning should be increased and intensified. The advantages are evident, above all in the prevention of environmental hazards and in the cutting of costs.

Key words (GeoRef Thesaurus, AGI): geologic maps, numerical maps, thematic maps, mineral resources, water supply, environmental geology, land use, urban planning, Iisalmi, Finland

*Maria Nikkarinen (editor), Geological Survey of Finland*
*Regional Office for Mid-Finland, P.O. Box 1237, FIN-70211 Kuopio, FINLAND*

*E-mail: maria.nikkarinen@gsf.fi*

# CONTENTS

# 1   INTRODUCTION

*Maria Nikkarinen*

The Geological Survey of Finland (GSF) undertakes nation-wide mapping of bedrock and surficial deposits as well as geophysical and geochemical surveys. The results of the mapping are published as separate sheets of traditional geological maps at different scales. The maps are a valuable source of information on properties of the ground that can be applied in land-use planning. To date, little use has been made of the information which can be extracted from conventional geological maps for the purposes of land-use planning and the special needs of environmental management, as all such information has to be interpreted by geological experts.

The thematic maps produced as a research and development project of the GSF were used to test the applicability of geological cartographic data to urban planning in a new, interpreted form. Iisalmi was selected as the pilot area because there are already various ongoing joint projects between the town and the GSF and also because sufficient digital data on various sectors of geology were available from the Iisalmi area. The project was carried out together with the planners and the environmental authority of Iisalmi town and the geologists. The working team decided on a scale of 1:50,000 because at that scale the whole town can be depicted graphically, and because the partial master plan of the rural area, which includes Iisalmi town, is at the same scale. In the end, maps covering the entire area of Iisalmi municipality (868 km$^2$) were produced on the following themes:

* natural resources
* water supply
* susceptibility of soil to acidification
* heavy metals in soil
* environmental impact on ground
* bedrock

In addition, an infiltration map was compiled for the 75 km$^2$ Kirmajärvi area in Ahmo, describing the capacity of the ground to absorb and bind waste water.

The maps are intended to serve as examples of the availability and applicability of interpreted geological information for one local government district but requirements of each municipality must be taken into account individually. The area mapped might comprise either the entire municipality or a larger or smaller part of it selected on the basis of the land-use plan. Geological basic information varies in both volume and accuracy from one part of Finland to another. The coverage of geological mapping is greatest in southern Finland and around urban centres. Data on surficial deposits are lacking for large areas of eastern Finland and Lapland.

In this account we describe the source material used in compiling the maps, discuss the grounds for the interpretations presented and examine the purposes for which the maps might be used. Only a small part of the area covered by a map-sheet is presented in the figures of thematic maps, although the original maps cover the whole municipality.

No new field mapping or studies were conducted for the thematic maps, which are based on data already stored in GSF's own databases. These data were then processed and interpreted and integrated with other geographical information on features such as roads, lakes and nature reserves. The quality of the interpretation depends on the accuracy of the mapping data, as no interpretation can produce results that are more accurate than the source material.

The need for geological information in urban planning, as a basis for both the decision-making process and the actual implementation of measures, is recognised more clearly than ever before. Geological information helps promote sustainable development in accordance with the provisions of

Fig. 1. Iisalmi is the centre of the northern Savo economic region.

the new Municipalities Act, which requires local authorities to seek to promote the welfare of the local population and the sustainable development of their region.

The objective of the municipalities of the northern Savo economic region for the year 2000 is a good and satisfying environment; for 2010 the objective is a region of sustainable development. The pilot projects carried out in this diverse environment, the achievements of geocollaboration and the information provided in this guide are of general interest and increasing importance.

## 1.1    Iisalmi in a nutshell

The thematic geological maps of Iisalmi depict the centre of a large economic region, of a town with robust industry, building, commerce and services as well as intensive forestry, agriculture — animal husbandry in particular — and other rural occupations. The area of Iisalmi comprises 868 km² and the number of inhabitants is 24,000 (Fig. 1).

The bedrock of the Iisalmi area is mainly Archaean, consisting of migmatitic tonalite gneiss more than 2,500 Ma in age (Paavola, 1991, Fig. 2), while some is among the oldest bedrock in Finland and possibly in the whole of Europe, with an age of over 3,100 Ma. Younger bedrock, i.e. Proterozoic schists and amphibolites, occurs in the western part of the area, forming the most prominent hilly areas in the regional relief, with a maximum elevation of 249 m a.s.l. Otherwise Iisalmi lies in a fairly flat area, probably a Neoproterozoic peneplain.

As is usually the case in Finland, a vast hiatus occurs between the Precambrian crystalline bedrock and loose surficial deposits from the Quaternary Ice Age. The Iisalmi area was repeatedly covered by the continental ice sheet during the Ice Age, and its cover of fine-grained till with > 5% clay and > 30% silt dates back to the last glaciation (Weichselian). The area is crossed by a NNW-SSE-trending esker deposited during the deglaciation, about 9500 years B.P., and forming part of an esker system which runs across the whole of Finland from Karelia to the Gulf of Bothnia.

After the Ice Age the region was submerged below the waters of the Baltic, which resulted in the deposition of a widespread and abundant cover of clay (Saarelainen 1995). The Iisalmi area emerged from the Baltic approximately 8,000 years ago as a consequence of isostatic land uplift, which is still going on at a rate of about 7 mm a year (Kukkonen and Sahala, 1988).

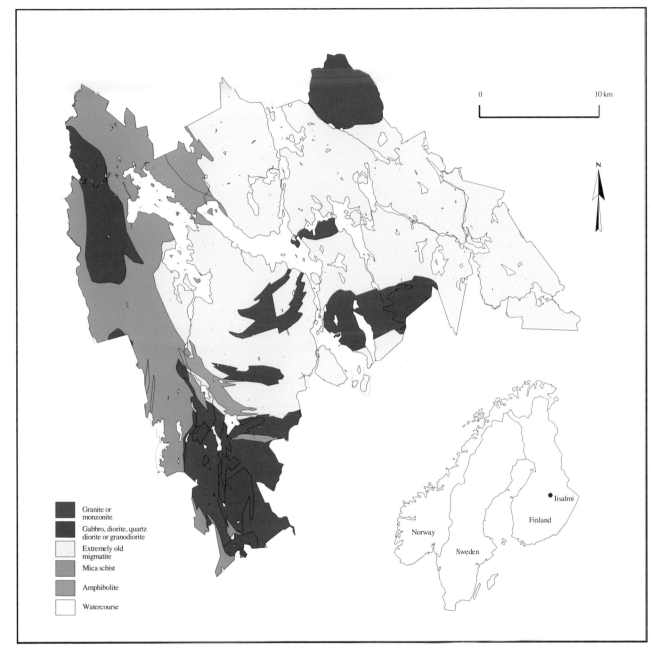

Fig. 2. Location of the town of Iisalmi and geological map of the area.

## 2 GEOLOGICAL THEMATIC MAPS OF IISALMI

### *Esa Kauniskangas*

Towards the end of 1992 the GSF acquired a Geographical Information System (GIS). Every office (Kuopio, Otaniemi and Rovaniemi) was provided with a UNIX workstation and an ARC/INFO® software licence for three simultaneous users. A Versatec colour plotter capable of drawing maps up to A0 size was also purchased for the Kuopio office.

With the introduction of the GIS interface in 1993, the Mid-Finland regional office was able to combine and analyse voluminous geological, geophysical and geochemical datasets to much better effect than previously. The thematic maps of Iisalmi were produced by interpreting the available digital datasets of the GSF and adding geographical information from other sources.

The GSF is currently digitising the maps of surficial deposits and bedrock for the FINGIS map-production system. The image-processing laboratory has interpreted images based on geophysical surveys and satellite data. Moreover, maps have been produced from analysis databases mainly using in-house graphics programs. The problem with these programs is that they allow flexible use of only one data type at the time.

### 2.1 Source materials

The source materials for thematic map production comprise maps of bedrock and Quaternary deposits, geophysical data files, and pointwise drilling and research data. The basic map of Quaternary geology at 1:20,000 depicts the distribution of unconsolidated soil types down to a depth of 1 m. The map of bedrock geology gives information on the composition of the Earth's crust beneath its layer of overburden. Low-altitude airborne geophysical survey data provide information on variations in the magnetic, electrical and radiometric properties of the bedrock. One important application of these airborne survey data is in the interpretation of shears to establish the location of fractures in the bedrock. Pointwise information on proper-ties is derived from geochemical soil and water analyses, drillcore data, the results of peat investigations and field observations of outcrops.

The town of Iisalmi provided us with its own vector and attribute datasets to be added to the maps. These data are on roads, place names, the location of industrial premises and well-water analyses. Use was also made of the restrictive data of protected areas in the Provincial State Office. In addition, information on the outlines of watercourses and fields in the town, and raster and vector elevation data were purchased from the National Land Survey of Finland. A Landsat satellite image of the Iisalmi area acquired by the GSF was also available.

### 2.2 Methods and interpretation

Several functions of the GIS were used to interpret geographical information for the municipal thematic maps. Each digital theme (soil permeability, shears in bedrock, etc.) is stored in the GIS program on different datasets. Thus, every interpreted theme can be used separately for the compilation of thematic maps (ESRI 1992). If only outlines of patterns are stored, we talk about a vector data model (Peuquet 1991). Data on maps of bedrock and Quaternary geology have been stored in this way. Raster data were also used in producing thematic maps. In the raster data model, each square — or pixel — is assigned a digital value which typically is geophysical or, say, the average height of the terrain at the site represented by the pixel. The GIS permits information on properties to be added to a point, line or area. For instance, on the map of surficial deposits, the soil code has been added to the code point of each area as their at-tribute data. Geological expertise is required to determine the appropriate classification for a thematic map.

Digital datasets may originally be in any coordinate system. ARC/INFO® can transform a map into the projection used by certain municipalities. However, it is advisable to employ the general coordinate system, which is also used when geographical locations are determined with automatic instruments (GPS). Note that when examining digital thematic maps the usability of the data depends on the recording scale. The GIS software allows a free choice of scale but data at 1:100,000 scale, for instance, cannot be used at 1:20,000 scale. An error of 1 mm (which is easily made when the data is digitised ) at 1:100,000 scale equals 100 m in the field, whereas the corresponding error at a digital scale of 1:20,000 is a mere 20 m. Positional errors may originate from mapping when marking observations on the base map as well as during simplifying and reducing from small-scale maps to the large-scale maps.

The attribute data of the GSF is stored mainly as relational databases. These include several tables in which the data are grouped in thematic entities. For instance, there may be several lithological observations, samples and chemical analyses of one outcrop. These data are stored in their own tables, which are linked to the table of general information on the outcrop. Attribute data is linked to the representation points on the map theme, after which they can be used in queries and spatial analyses.

Selection of areas is one of the most common analytical functions of the GIS. The selections are made either by outlining the target on a map displayed on a screen or by searching for targets satisfying certain conditions on the basis of the attribute data. Other routine functions are queries about the properties of an object and the calculation of statistical parameters for target populations. The program automatically computes the surfaces of the areas when the outlines of the areas are changed. Datasets can be divided up into smaller pieces on the basis of the border line of any arbitrary polygon. In this way all the datasets used — in both raster and vector forms — can be divided up as wished, for instance, along the municipal border line. Influence or buffer zones can be calculated around points, lines and areas. On the environmental map a 100 m-wide zone on each side of the road was calculated for the areas of influence of the main Iisalmi roads (Fig. 8). The risk areas in this zone were then interpreted. The procedure can be applied in the search for a suitable site for industrial facilities by requiring that they should be located on a certain type of ground and at a certain distance from a road or watercourse.

Elevation data can be utilised in various ways with the GIS. In a plain-like obliquely illuminated elevation model the scale is accurate (see the heavy metal map Fig. 5). Topography can also be shown in perspective presentation, in which case any other information can be printed on the surface of the model. The scale of this presentation, however, is not accurate. Slope gradients and the masses of surficial deposits located between two levels can be calculated from the elevation data.

The raster base map of the National Land Survey of Finland can be used as the background for thematic maps. Its lines can be made visible through the other plotted data when the map is printed out. The base map must be obtained at the suitable scale. In this case, a 1:50,000 scale raster base map would be required, but such maps are not available for the whole of Finland. There is, in this case, no point in using a more accurate 1:20,000 raster base map as the detection limit of the output devices is inadequate for reproducing small patterns properly. Datasets in the vector form do not pose this problem but the price of the licence is considerably higher than that of the raster data.

# 3  NATURAL RESOURCES

*Keijo Nenonen*

**The map of natural resources depicts the location of potential soil and bedrock resources. The information on these maps is indicative and intended for the needs of master plans and regional plans. Detailed information on resources must always be established site-by-site.**

The lithological information on the natural resources map (Fig. 3) derives from the bedrock map covering the whole area. Data on surficial deposits are more accurate for the central part of the map-sheet area, where basic mapping of Quaternary deposits in scale 1:20,000 has been carried out, but less so for the eastern and western parts of the area. The most important natural resources in this area are sand, gravel, clay, energy-peat and groundwater. Groundwater data are presented separately on a water supply map (Fig. 3). The GSF archives contain data on reserves of gravel, sand and energy-peat. The bedrock resources marked on the map are rock types used as dimension stones, in this case granite, monzonite and dolerite (diabase).

The Iisalmi area is exceptional in that all its natural resources have industrial use. Sand and gravel are utilised by prefabricated-unit plants, clay has been used by the brickworks and peat by the Iisalmi power plant. At present, however, the energy-peat comes from bogs located in other municipalities. The dimension stone industry has a long history in Ylä-Savo.

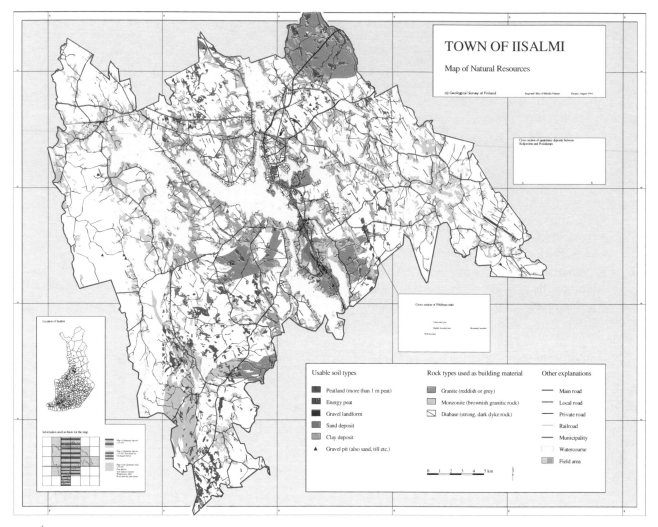

Fig. 3 The map of natural resources. Model of the original map (not in original scale).

## 3.1 Exploitable sediments and soils

### 3.1.1 Gravel and sand

The gravel and sand resources above the groundwater level in Iisalmi were assessed as a joint project of the GSF and the Finnish National Road Administration (Tikkanen and Niemelä 1975). Some of the sand and gravel occurrences assessed in the 1970´s have already been exhausted. In the course of the basic mapping of surficial deposits new data have accumulated for the assessment of mineral resources. It is now known, for instance, that the Iisalmi area has 1,392 hectares of sand and gravel deposits with 1.2 million m$^3$ of gravel suitable for crushing, 6.4 million m$^3$ of gravelly material and 60.2 million m$^3$ of sandy material above groundwater level.

The most important formation for gravel resources on a regional scale is the Iisalmi esker, which traverses the whole country and at Iisalmi contains five formations of total 49 million m$^3$ sand and gravel. The largest formation hosts most of the extraction sites in the Iisalmi area, although a considerable amount of the 1 million m$^3$ of crushable and 3 million m$^3$ of gravelly material has already been used. Exploitation of the Iisalmi esker is restricted by the fact that the esker is an important groundwater reserve for the town of Iisalmi. Outside the main esker formation there are small littoral deposits and other sorted formations, most of which contain sandy material and small amounts of gravelly material. The volume of sand reserves above groundwater level in these formations varies greatly depending on the depth of the formation; the average is about 100,000 m$^3$. Small sand reserve formations have local importance for villages and the maintenance of local roads, and their exploitation seldom poses a threat to key aquifers.

### 3.1.2 Clay

The clay marked on the map (Fig. 3) includes both silt and clay deposits, which are usually cultivated. The Soinlahti brickworks north of Iisalmi is the only factory in the area that uses clay. Owing to the recession in the construction sector the brickworks has been at a standstill since 1993. The brickmaking properties of clays in the environment of Iisalmi were studied comprehensively in the 1970's and 1980's (Kukkonen and Sahala 1988). Of the clays investigated, 12.5% were in the highest brick clay class, containing a 30–40% clay fraction and 35–45% silt, the remainder being fine sand; 26.5% of the samples taken from test areas satisfied the technical criteria of brick clays. According to Romu (1978), the silty clays of Iisalmi are well suited for brick production as shown by their shrinkage in drying and moulding moisture values and the results of brick-burning tests. Before technical exploitation is feasible, however, the clay needs to be homogenised and worked, and sand must be added to eliminate differences in the natural clays. The dry surficial part of the clay deposits, i.e. the dry crust, can often be used as raw material for bricks; the blue clay beneath the dry crust, however, which is water-bearing and in a reduced state, cannot. The clay deposits at Iisalmi will thus be able to continue to provide brickworks with suitable raw material.

### 3.1.3 Peat

Marked on the map are 14 mires suitable for energy-peat production (Fig. 3). In the west of the town there are large mires that have not yet been assessed. The best mire is 77 ha with 620,000 m$^3$ of its 1.25 million in-situ m$^3$ peat resources suitable for energy production. The majority of the other energy-peat mires marked on the map have potential for small-scale production, e.g. of sods, should there be a commercial demand for such peat.

The Iisalmi electricity and district heating plant generates heat mainly from peat transported from the peat production areas in the neigbouring province. The plant burns about 100,000 m$^3$ of peat and produces 81,468 MWh district heat energy per year (in 1993). Peat accounts for 60% of the energy production of Iisalmi.

As part of the assessment of peat resources in Finland, 26% of mires in the Iisalmi area have now been investigated (Lappalainen and Hänninen 1993). The area contains 21 mires with a total area exceeding 50 ha. The average depth of the mires studied is about 1.1 m and the verified amount of peat 7.8 million m$^3$. It has been estimated that the mires in the Iisalmi area contain a total of 30.1 million m$^3$ of peat.

Most of the mires in the Iisalmi area have been drained or otherwise altered by human activity; none of them are in the national peatland protection programme. Mires account for a good 10% of the total land area. Associated with peatlands and drained lakes there are gyttja and mull areas, some of which may be excellent sources of raw materials for landscaping and soil improvement. Detailed information on mires suitable for energy-peat production in each municipality is available in the mire register and peat archives of the GSF.

Fig. 4. The church of Sonkajärvi has been built of the local diabase. Photo Eero Pitkänen.

## 3.2   Exploitable rocks

*Jorma Paavola*

The bedrock in the Iisalmi urban area is not very promising for prospecting but it has potential for use as dimension stones and aggregate. The map of natural resources (Fig. 3) depicts the rocks that have been used for this purpose. Certain rocks may contain asbestos, uranium or abundant micas, all obstacles to the use of the rocks as aggregate; these can, however, be taken into account at the initial stage of exploitation. Studies of dimension stones always require a great deal of painstaking work on rock exposures, as the quality and solidity of the rock must be carefully verified before quarrying starts. An advantage of Finnish dimension stones is their good resistance to urban pollution.

### 3.2.1 Dimension stones

The basic requirements for a good dimension stone are solidity, colour and homogeneity. Recently, however, demand on the world market has grown for rocks with vivid patterns and in many different shades. The eastern and southern parts of Iisalmi offer the likeliest sources of exploitable dimension stones (Fig. 3). Banded and multicoloured migmatite predominates in the Iisalmi area. Being sufficiently solid and colourful it has some potential as a dimension stone. As well as migmatites, there are several evenly coloured granite, granodiorite and quartz diorite intrusions that have long been used for plinths, walls and paving. At one deposit

there is an unusual brownish monzonite with scattered spherical orbicular feldspar grains.

Dark rocks have traditionally been used as gravestones, and demand for them has always been assured. In the central part of Iisalmi there is a dark hornblende pyroxenite (Fig. 3). Many diabase dykes, too, are dark and thus the search for dimension stones focuses on dark diabases. Exploitation of diabases, however, is often prevented by the fracturing of the rocks. At one target there is a diabase quarry worked by Sukevan Kivi Oy. Visitors can admire the local diabase in the church of Sonkajärvi, which is built almost entirely of this rock (Fig. 4). The diabase of Varpaisjärvi (commercial name: black granite) is widely known.

### 3.2.2 Aggregate

Owing to the exhaustion of gravel reserves planned for exploitation and to the progress made in quarrying and crushing, rock aggregate is now commonly used in many applications. The quality criteria set by users of rock aggregate differ widely. For pavement the Finnish National Road Administration needs rock which is highly resistant to wear by anti-skid studs. In railway construction the emphasis is on the tolerance of aggregate to vibration. In the cement industry it is important that the particles of the aggregate used should be weather resistant and that they should bind tightly to ce-

Fig. 5. Adjacent to the Iisalmi landfill is a large aggregate extraction site at which the Finnish National Road Administration quarries and crushes migmatite and diabase. Photo Kai Jägerholm.

ment. A preliminary estimate of the usability of rocks for aggregate can be obtained by studying their minerals. For the final assessment the rock is submitted to various tests to establish quality values and form classes. There are four strength and form classes. Based on the weakest property, these classes do not depend on each other.

Adjacent to the Iisalmi landfill there is a large aggregate extraction site at which the Finnish National Road Administration quarries and crushes migmatite and diabase; both make first-class pavement rock with the highest quality grade and are suitable for roads with heavy traffic (Fig. 5). Elsewhere in the Iisalmi area there are other diabases that deserve to be studied as a potential source of rock aggregate. As well as quality, transport costs should be taken into account when evaluating such sites. Long transport distances restrict the exploitation of even high-quality rocks if quarries are located far from urban centres. It is important that each site should be submitted to a separate exhaus-

tive study. Investigations may show that a rock resembling a good one in appearance and mineral composition is, in fact, fragile and friable and thus useless as aggregate.

### 3.2.3 Gemstones

The selection of a rock for use as gemstones or ornaments is very much a matter of taste. Cut with skill, the most unpretentious stone may be transformed into an object of great beauty.

In the target area there there is a quarry from which a greenish quartz- epidote rock has been extracted for jewellery. This rock has gained wide recognition and is even mentioned in the book of Finnish gemstones. Garnet is a well-known gemstone, and the garnetiferous amphibolite in the eastern part of Iisalmi may have potential as such for the rock contains plenty of reddish-purple garnet grains. In addition, one quarry in the area used to produce vein quartz for the glass industry.

## 4   WATER SUPPLY

*Esa Kauniskangas and Keijo Nenonen*

**The water supply map depicts the areas that are geologically suitable for the formation and retention of groundwater. The map can be used in the general planning of the water supply of urban and rural areas.**

Esker aquifers were picked out from the digital surficial deposit datasets and databases and plotted on the map in bright green (Fig. 6). In these areas groundwater is formed in abundance and its flow rate is high. Good local aquifers, i.e. sandy areas,

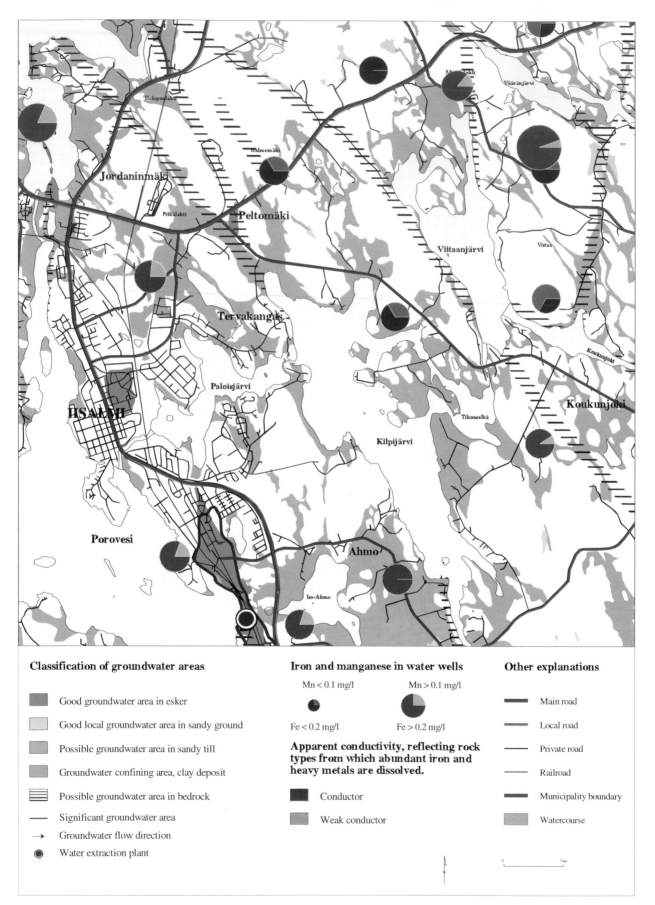

**Classification of groundwater areas**

- Good groundwater area in esker
- Good local groundwater area in sandy ground
- Possible groundwater area in sandy till
- Groundwater confining area, clay deposit
- Possible groundwater area in bedrock
- ——— Significant groundwater area
- → Groundwater flow direction
- ◉ Water extraction plant

**Iron and manganese in water wells**

Mn < 0.1 mg/l    Mn > 0.1 mg/l

Fe < 0.2 mg/l    Fe > 0.2 mg/l

**Apparent conductivity, reflecting rock types from which abundant iron and heavy metals are dissolved.**

- Conductor
- Weak conductor

**Other explanations**

- ——— Main road
- ══ Local road
- ——— Private road
- ——— Railroad
- ━━━ Municipality boundary
- Watercourse

Fig. 6. An excerpt of the map of water supply. (This is only a small part of the area presented in the original map).

were marked on the map in pale green. Sandy areas, possibly with sufficient groundwater to meet the needs of local households, are marked separately. High-quality groundwater may also occur in sandy till areas, provided that the till deposits lie on sufficiently steep slopes. Retentive and poorly permeable clay areas are marked in blue. Other valuable sources of groundwater are bedrock fractures, marked on the map as a horizontally striated zone. Bedrock groundwater is an excellent alternative source of water in areas without eskers or other surficial deposits suitable for water intake.

As well as outlining the areas suitable for groundwater formation, the map presents groundwater quality factors on the basis of geological information. Apparent conductivity was calculated from low-altitude electrical survey data, and the anomalies were then divided into conductors and weak conductors, marked on the map in purple. In the Iisalmi area, the strong conductors are very small and there are not even many weak conductors, implying a scarcity of black schists and rocks with iron sulphides. The strong conductors occur in the immediate vicinity of Iisalmi, in the neigbouring municipalities. If the bedrock contains abundant iron and heavy metals, the average concentration of these elements is high in soil, too, and under certain redox conditions they dissolve in groundwater.

Previous analytical data on water from dug wells, drilled wells and springs in Iisalmi were available and were stored in the Geological Survey's GIS. The iron and manganese concentrations in well waters are depicted on the map with circle symbols. A bluish-green circle indicates analyses in which the iron (Fe) and manganese (Mn) concentrations meet the quality criteria of good potable water (Ministry of Social and Health affairs, 1991). The orange symbol indicates that the concentration of at least one of these two elements in well water exceeds the maximum permissible level. The maximum target concentration is 0.2 mg/l for iron and 0.1 mg/l for manganese. The symbol grows in size with the increase in the sum concentration. The highest iron and manganese concentrations are in waters from the Spa named Runni in the northwestern part of the municipality. Factors such as well type and the material of which the well is constructed may also affect water quality.

The water supply map also shows the groundwater reservoirs delineated by the Kuopio Water and Environment District, the flow directions of the groundwater, and the water intake plants and pumping stations currently in operation.

## 4.1 Quality of soil groundwater and controlling factors

In sparsely populated areas, the quality of water in wells is often controlled by factors related to the type of soil. As a rule, the quality of groundwater is high in coarse sand and gravel deposits, and both quality and yield are further improved by steep slopes and a gradient in the groundwater table. At the margins of clay deposits, the iron and manganese concentrations in groundwater in clay-covered till and in low-yield wells in fines-rich till tend to exceed the quality criteria of good potable water. The area of sandy till in the south of the map-sheet is good for the groundwater supply of a rural area. The yield and quality of water in wells in sandy till are better than in the other till areas of Iisalmi, which are mainly composed of fines-rich till. Note that the permeability of a sandy till (K = $10^{-6}$–$10^{-7}$ m/s) is comparable to that of fine sand, whereas the permeability of clayey fines-rich till (K = $10^{-9}$–$10^{-10}$ m/s) is approximately the same as that of clayey soil.

The chemical state of water (pH and Eh) is decisive for the ability of groundwater to dissolve iron, manganese and other impurities from soil and bedrock. Groundwater that flows slowly under an isolating layer of clay, silt and peat is reduced due to consumption of oxygen by the decomposition of organic matter (Lahermo et al. 1990). The groundwater in coarse soils and deep bedrock joints under the isolation layer is therefore in a reduced state and usually of poor quality. Oxygen-bearing groundwater that flows rapidly in coarse soils and shallow open bedrock fractures and joints is fresh and seldom contains iron and manganese in harmful concentrations. It is important that those responsible for planning sites for water intake plants and wells to be dug in soil take into account the degradation of groundwater quality caused by latrines, cowsheds, waste water infiltration wells, sewers, field fertilization, forage stacks and landfills. As shown by the GSF's national assessment of groundwater resources (Lahermo et al. 1990), the quality of water in private wells in sparsely populated areas varies appreciably and in 12% of the well-water samples tested the concentration of $NO_3$ exceeded 30 mg/l. Old wells in poor condition dug in soil and lined with stone or wood in eastern and southeastern Finland were particularly prone to pollution. Salts used to prevent slipperiness and to bind dust on roads pollutes groundwater in the vicinity of roads and houses. The water in roadside wells may contain several tens of millilitres of salt per litre.

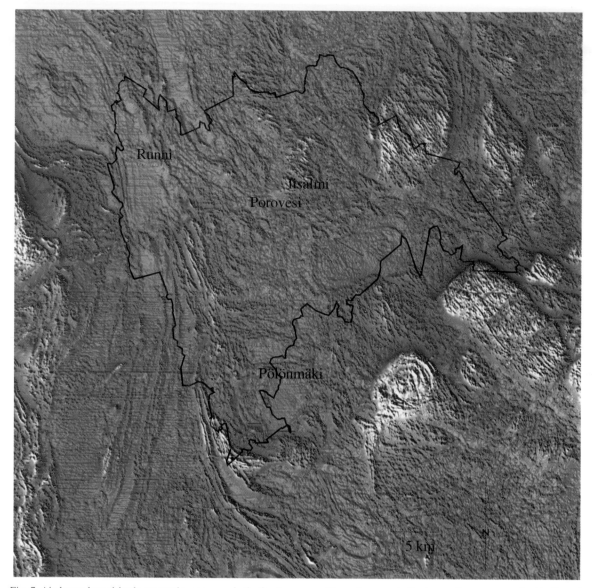

Fig. 7. Air-borne low altitude magnetic map reveals the fracture zones (the red arrows indicate two fracture zones in this figure).

## 4.2 Groundwater potential of bedrock and controlling factors

Shear zones and strong electrical conductors are marked on the map (Fig. 6). The fracture zones are important for the occurrence of bedrock groundwater, because water moves in them as it does in eskers. In bedrock fractures covered by a sheltering overburden the groundwater is protected from human impact and the pollution caused by environmental hazards no matter how grave. The groundwater in fractures is old, often several hudred and sometimes even thousands of years old (Lamminen 1995). Wells drilled into bedrock fracture zones can satisfy the water needs of large urban centres, and in sparsely populated areas are an important alternative source of water for villages. Not all the fractures marked on the map contain groundwater, as some of them have healed or weathered into impermeable gouge (Fig. 7). The true water potential of a fracture zone can only be assessed with sounding and drilling.

Electrical conductors indicate the presence of sulphides in bedrock. When they weather, sulphides, which contain metals and sulphur, dissolve, thus increasing the iron, sulphur and manganese concentrations in groundwaters. Hence, the mineral-bearing water of the Runni Spa, for instance, derives from a sulphide-bearing bedrock zone marked as an electrical conductor on the map. The water at Runni contains 24 mg/l Fe, whereas most well waters in the Iisalmi area assay less than 1 mg/l Fe.

The main problems of bedrock groundwater are high iron and manganese concentrations and the salinity of bedrock wells. Such wells should not be made too deep, as below 100 m the probability of encountering saline groundwater rises (Hyyppä 1984 , Lamminen 1995). Saline groundwaters are usually remnants of ancient sea water, and at depths exceeding 300 m there may be saline waters that were generated by geological processes during the formation and alteration of rocks. Water satisfying the quality criteria can usually be obtained by drilling wells into bedrock that contains numerous horizontal joints or shears, is free from sulphides and is covered by coarse-grained overburden. Granitic rocks and schists rich in feldspar and lacking sulphides generally contain high-quality bedrock groundwater. Black schists and mica schists with

graphite and sulphides, and gneisses with abundant weathered mica should generally be avoided. Black schists that contain metal-bearing sulphides have been documented to pose an environmental threat when occurring at the groundwater area (Piispanen and Nykyri 1996).

The radon content of analysed groundwater samples in the Iisalmi area have generally been found to be below the Finnish mean content (Voutilainen 1994). The result is understandable since airborne radiometric data (gamma radiation) do not indicate any uranium deposits in the area. The uranium content of till is 2,5 mg/kg. The mean content in till in Finland is 3,3 mg/kg (Koljonen 1992).

## 5   HEAVY METAL CONCENTRATION IN SOIL

*Maria Nikkarinen*

**The map of heavy-metal concentration indicates the natural concentrations of these metals in till fines. Variations in the concentrations are mainly due to variations in bedrock lithology. The map can be used as a source of background information in assessing land pollution and in establishing areas with natural heavy-metal concentrations that pose a potential risk to health.**

The map illustrating natural heavy-metal concentrations in soil (Fig. 8) is based on data collected by the national geochemical mapping programme undertaken by the GSF (Salminen 1995). In the mapping of tills, samples were taken from a depth of 1.5–2 m at a density of one sample per 4 km². To improve the representativeness the final sample was made by combining 3 or 4 subsamples. The finest fraction, < 0.06 mm, was screened for chemical analysis. The samples were leached in aqua regia and analysed by inductively coupled plasma-atomic emission spectrometry (ICP-AES). Aqua regia dissolves elements mainly from micas, clay minerals and sulphides; the procedure gives almost the total concentrations of base metals in the sample (Räisänen et. al. 1992, Niskavaara 1995).

The variation in the metal concentrations in till is due to variations in rock and soil types. Heavy metals are not major components of the Earth's crust but are trace elements making up less than 2% of its mass.

The main sector using the results of geochemical mapping has traditionally been exploration, because ores commonly cause anomalous element concentrations in till fines. With the increase in environmental awareness, natural element concentrations in soil are also used to assess soil pollution. In low concentrations, some of the metals are essential for organisms

— both humans, animals and plants — but in high concentrations are deleterious or even toxic. Cadmium, mercury, lead and arsenic, all of which occur in bedrock and in soil (which derives from bedrock), are considered among the most harmful metals.

The Ministry of the Environment has issued recommended limits for assessing soil pollution. Areas are designated as polluted if, due to human activity, harmful substances have accumulated in them to an extent hazardous to health, the environment or structures (U. Jeltsch 1990, Puolanne et al. 1994). When the impact of human activities is assessed, it is necessary to know the natural concentrations, as these vary greatly.

In soil, metals are bound by nature to different types of particles, or minerals. It is the properties of these minerals, their susceptibility to weathering in particular, and the conditions prevailing in the soil that determine whether a metal dissolves in soil water from a mineral and, if it does, to what extent, or whether it remains insoluble in the mineral. Metals pose a health hazard only when they participate in the natural cycle becoming bioavailable and entering drinking water or the food chain in harmful concentrations.

The heavy metal map shows the natural variation in copper (blue), nickel (red) and zinc (yellow) concentrations in till in the Iisalmi area (Fig. 8). The bigger the symbol, the higher the total concentrations of elements; each sector of the circle indicates the proportion of a single element. The concentration symbols are marked on a map base depicting the relief. Cadmium and mercury have not been analysed in the regional gechemical mapping programme and the contents of lead and arsenic in the Iisalmi area are below the detection limit.

Natural concentrations of heavy metals are low in

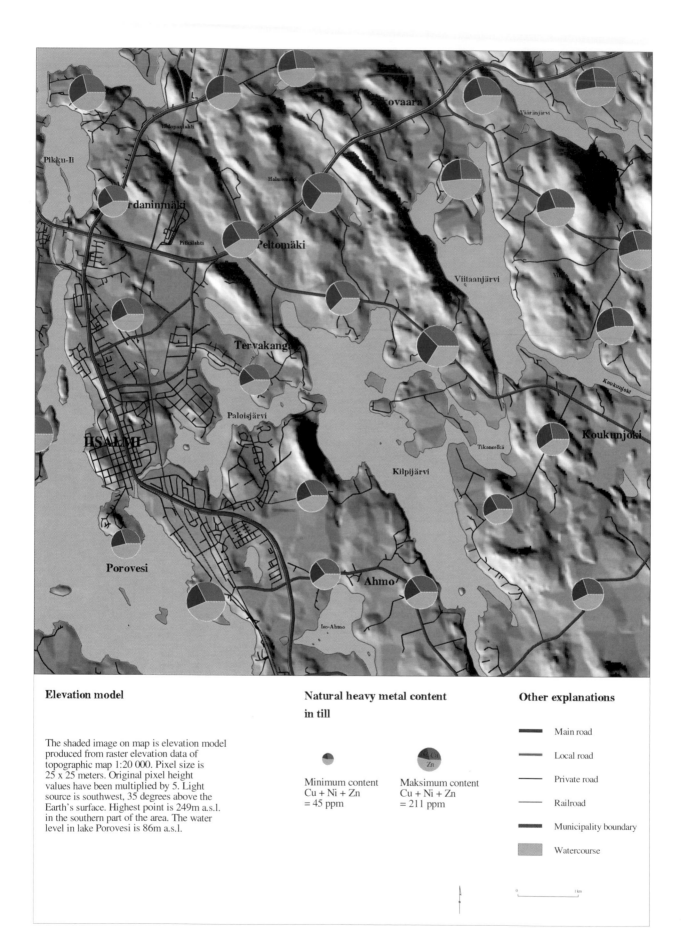

## Elevation model

The shaded image on map is elevation model
produced from raster elevation data of
topographic map 1:20 000. Pixel size is
25 x 25 meters. Original pixel height
values have been multiplied by 5. Light
source is southwest, 35 degrees above the
Earth's surface. Highest point is 249m a.s.l.
in the southern part of the area. The water
level in lake Porovesi is 86m a.s.l.

## Natural heavy metal content in till

Minimum content
Cu + Ni + Zn
= 45 ppm

Maksimum content
Cu + Ni + Zn
= 211 ppm

## Other explanations

Main road

Local road

Private road

Railroad

Municipality boundary

Watercourse

Fig. 8 An excerpt of the map of Natural Cu, Ni, Zn content in soil.

Table 1. Trace metal concentrations in the fine fraction (< 0.06 mm) of till in the Iisalmi area and in the whole country.

| Element | Iisalmi | | Whole country* |
| | range mg/kg | mean mg/kg | mean mg/kg |
| --- | --- | --- | --- |
| Cobalt Co | 5.6–22.4 | 12.4 | 9.3 |
| Chromium Cr | 16.2–71.2 | 36.5 | 39.1 |
| Copper Cu | 12.4–94.3 | 28.3 | 28.3 |
| Nickel Ni | 10.4–53.6 | 22.3 | 36.3 |
| Phosphorus P | 724–2190 | 959.2 | 734.0 |
| Zinc Zn | 15.9–105.0 | 46.6 | 36.8 |

* Salminen 1995

the Iisalmi area, being only slightly above the average for the whole country (Table 1). Even the maximum concentrations of copper, nickel and zinc do not exceed the maximum permissible levels set by the Ministry of the Environment (Table 2). The distribution of metals, however, is uneven and thus there are some places with high natural concentra-

Table 2. Values used to assess soil pollution (Puolanne et al. 1994).

| Metal | Normative value mg/kg | Limit mg/kg |
| --- | --- | --- |
| Copper Cu | 100 | 400 |
| Nickel Ni | 60 | 200 |
| Zinc Zn | 150 | 700 |

tions in municipalities adjoining Iisalmi (Fig. 9).

The normative value for multiple land use refers to the concentration of a hazardous substance which is considered harmless to humans and the environment. In this case there are no restrictions on land use and the disposition of earth masses. If the normative value is exceeded, the impacts on the environment should be assessed. If the limit is exceeded, land use must be restricted in the area to ensure that any increase in the concentration of the substance in soil will not endanger health or the environment.

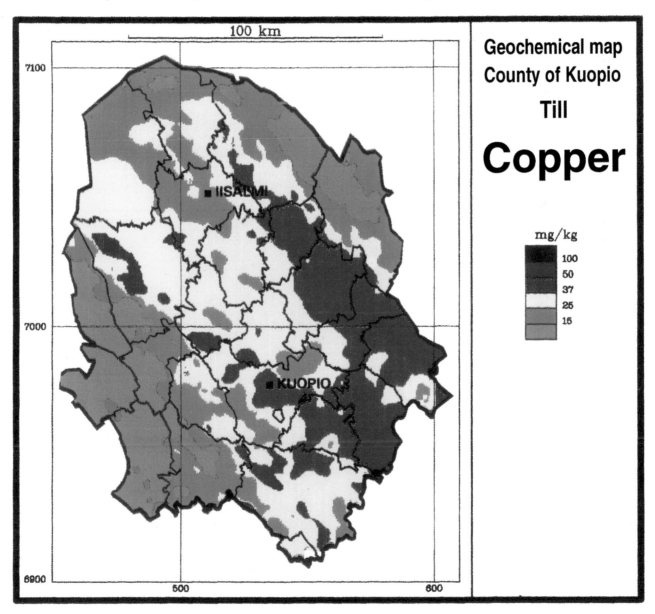

Fig. 9. Copper content in the Kuopio county region.

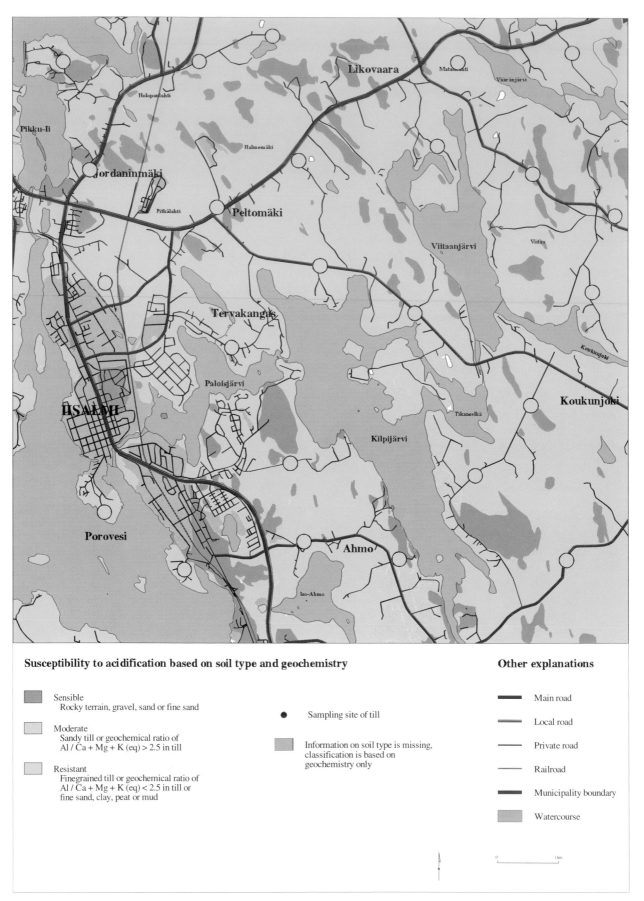

**Susceptibility to acidification based on soil type and geochemistry**

**Other explanations**

Sensible
Rocky terrain, gravel, sand or fine sand

● Sampling site of till

Moderate
Sandy till or geochemical ratio of
Al / Ca + Mg + K (eq) > 2.5 in till

Information on soil type is missing,
classification is based on
geochemistry only

Resistant
Finegrained till or geochemical ratio of
Al / Ca + Mg + K (eq) < 2.5 in till or
fine sand, clay, peat or mud

Main road

Local road

Private road

Railroad

Municipality boundary

Watercourse

Fig. 10. An excerpt of the map of susceptibility to acidification.

# 6  SUSCEPTIBILITY OF SOIL TO ACIDIFICATION

*Marja Liisa Räisänen*

**The map of the susceptibility of soil to acidification reveals the extent to which the mineral soil beneath the podzolic pedon slows down groundwater acidification. The map serves the needs of land-use planning when a site has to be found for operations that will accelerate soil acidification.**

The ability of the soil to retard the changes associated with acidification that impair the quality of groundwater is controlled by several factors, e.g. climate, vegetation, the geochemical composition and the water permeability of the soil. In Finland, the surface layer of soil is naturally acidic due to podzolization. A podzol develops when acidic water from the humus layer and plant roots´ activity leaches nutrients, iron and aluminium from the soil minerals. Weathering of micas and Mg-bearing clay minerals during podzolisation is the predominant process leading to the production of nutrients such as Ca, Mg and K when carbonates are lacking (Räisänen et al. 1992).

Some minerogenic nutrients are stored in the humus and ash-grey eluvial layers in a form useful for plants; some are leached to lower layers and some into groundwater. In natural acidification only small amounts of useful nutrients are washed and transported to lower soil horizons and further into groundwater. Another distinctive feature is the precipitation of aluminium and iron and other heavy metals as rusty-coloured bands of almost insoluble compounds in topsoil horizons (illuvial layer). In highly permeable soils, metals are precipitated at even greater depths in mineral soil strata above the groundwater table. The natural acidity of mineral soils decreases from the top layers downwards. Acid rainwater leaches nutrients such as calcium (Ca), magnesium (Mg) and potassium (K) from humus and underlying mineral soil, and, in the event of an increase in acidification, harmful aluminium (Al) too. The amount of nutrients and aluminium rebound to topsoil layers and leached down into lower horizons and the groundwater depends primarily on the reactivity, composition and permeability of the soil. These are the key factors that control the susceptibility of soil to acidification (Räisänen 1989).

In the Iisalmi area this susceptibility was assessed using the map of Quaternary deposits at 1:20,000 scale and the geochemical data on till fines (Fig. 10). The till samples for geochemical mapping were taken from a depth of about 2 m, whereas in the mapping of Quaternary deposits the soil type was determined at a depth of about 1 m. The ratio of the aluminium concentration to the sum of calcium, magnesium and potassium concentrations (calculated as equivalent weights = eq) was used as a chemical index $Al/(Ca+Mg+K)$ to assess the acidification susceptibility of till. Analyses were made selectively on the mica and clay mineral fractions of the till fines, as their composition is the main factor controlling the neutralization of acidity. The higher the concentrations of calcium, magnesium and potassium (a low ratio) in the mica and clay mineral fraction, the better the soil can prevent acidification from reaching the groundwater. The ratio also describes the contribution made by the dissolution and precipitation reactions of aluminium to the prevention of acidification. Should acidification be intensified, harmful aluminium may occur in tills with high concentrations of aluminium in relation to those of calcium, magnesium and potassium (Räisänen et al. 1992).

Highly permeable esker terrains and rocky areas (either exposed or covered by only shallow overburden) are the most acid sensitive. As the rate of rainwater flow in these areas is higher than in fine sandy and silty soils, reactions between runoff and mineral soil are minimal. In eskers the rate of acidification of groundwater and lower soil horizons is controlled by the alternation and thickness of coarse and fine strata and the thickness and reactivity of the forest podzol horizon. Sandy till soils and till soils with $Al/(Ca+Mg+K)$ exceeding 2.5 have a moderate capacity to prevent acidification from intensifying. The capacity is low if the ratio exeeds 5. If the soil in an area is composed of till fines, fine sand, clay, peat and gyttja, acidification is effectively neutralized. Such soils are also capable of binding toxic metals and compounds leached from the topsoil and thus of preventing excessive groundwater acidification and pollution.

The map of susceptibility to acidification mainly depicts the capacity of the soil beneath the forest podzol horizon to mitigate the adverse effects of acidification on groundwater (Fig. 10). The soil and geochemical classification is only a rough one based on general properties of soil types in the country as a whole. The regional differences should therefore be considered merely as indicative. Although the geochemical properties, soil type distribution and permeability of the parent soil are reflected in the chemical properties of the podzolized mineral soil layer, the map does not show directly the acid sensitivity of the humus layer. The map was commissioned by the Environmental Office of Kuopio province. These thematic maps may thus find better use in the classification of areas within provinces than in internal municipal planning.

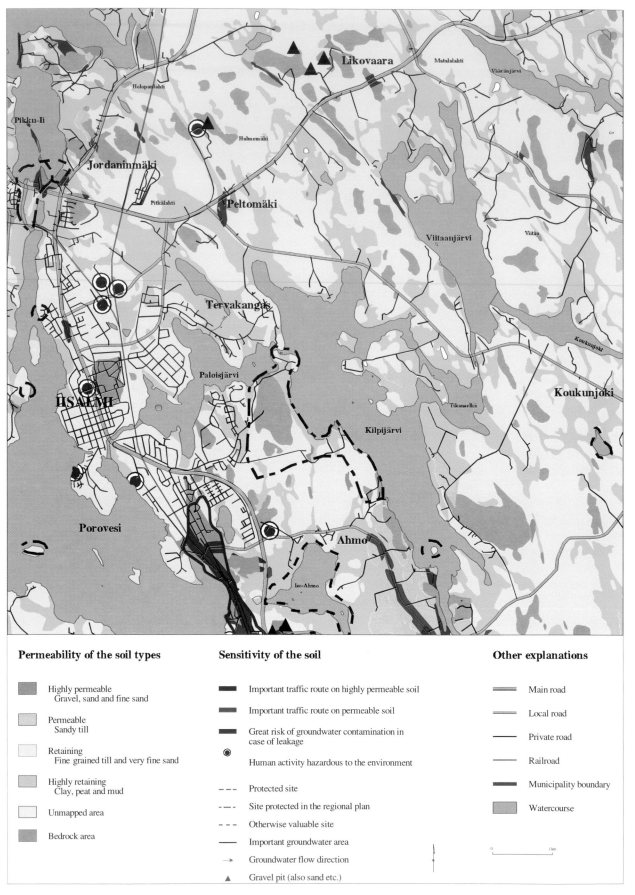

**Permeability of the soil types**

Highly permeable
Gravel, sand and fine sand

Permeable
Sandy till

Retaining
Fine grained till and very fine sand

Highly retaining
Clay, peat and mud

Unmapped area

Bedrock area

**Sensitivity of the soil**

Important traffic route on highly permeable soil

Important traffic route on permeable soil

Great risk of groundwater contamination in case of leakage

Human activity hazardous to the environment

Protected site

Site protected in the regional plan

Otherwise valuable site

Important groundwater area

Groundwater flow direction

Gravel pit (also sand etc.)

**Other explanations**

Main road

Local road

Private road

Railroad

Municipality boundary

Watercourse

Fig. 11. An excerpt of the map of soil and groundwater vulnerability.

Fig. 12. The main road lies on permeable soil type in some places of Iisalmi area. In the event of accident the risk for ground water pollution is great in such areas. Photo Kai Jägerholm.

## 7  MAP OF SOIL AND GROUNDWATER VULNERABILITY

*Esa Kauniskangas, Keijo Nenonen and Maria Nikkarinen*

**This map shows the variation in soil permeability, which is one of the main factors determining the extent of environmental damage and the risk of groundwater contamination. Use can be made of the map in assessing environmental impacts, in risk management and in land-use planning. The best results are obtained when precautionary measures are taken.**

Important geological factors pertinent to the management of environmental risks are the water-holding capacity of soil, bedrock fractures, landscape patterns and differences in elevation. On the geological environmental impact map, areas differing in soil type are classified by permeability. In the event of an accident, the highly permeable gravel and sand areas marked in red are at special risk, as they are almost incapable of preventing hazardous substances from infiltrating the soil and reaching the groundwater. Areas of sandy till, marked on the map in a somewhat lighter red than the highly permeable areas, are permeable. Areas with water-retention capacity are indicated in various shades of green. Retaining and highly retaining soils are fines-rich tills, fine sand, clay, peat and

gyttja (Fig. 11).

The multivariate analysis capability of the GIS was used to combine the environmental impact map. Traffic presents present a major environmental risk in Iisalmi. Routes with heavy traffic and used for transporting chemicals in large quantities were separated from the road network (Fig. 12). A 200 m-wide zone was established around them and a systematic search was made for all sections of the zones that lie on either highly permeable or permeable soil. These areas were then marked on the map in purple shades. The criteria in the search for areas with a very high risk of groundwater contamination were based on soil permeability data and interpreted information on shear zones in bedrock. Hazardous substances may migrate freely along open bedrock shears for long distances from the site of an accident. The outcome of the analysis is depicted in bright red to attract attention.

The geological environmental impact map clearly reveals the areas that require more detailed investigation and better protection, for example, when buildings or roads are planned. The best use can be made of the maps by directing construction to risk-free areas, which are shaded green.

### 7.1  Water permeability of soil

The capacity of soil to hold water is directly proportional to the grain-size distribution, struc-

ture and stratification of surficial deposits. In the coarse gravel of eskers, the infiltration and flow of

Table 3. Coefficients of water permeability and oil-retention capacity of soils.

| Soil | Coefficient of of water permeability k (m/s) | Oil retension capacity (l/m³) | | |
|---|---|---|---|---|
| | | Gasoline | Diesel | Light fuel oil |
| Gravel | $10^{-1}$–$10^{-3}$ | 2,5–4 | 5–8 | 10–16 |
| Sand | $10^{-2}$–$10^{-6}$ | 4–13 | 8–25 | 16–50 |
| Silt and sandy till | $10^{-5}$–$10^{-9}$ | 20 | 40 | 80 |
| Clayey till | < $10^{-9}$ | d o e s  n o t  i n f i l t r a t e | | |
| Clay | < $10^{-9}$ | d o e s  n o t  i n f i l t r a t e | | |

water and harmful liquids proceeds almost unhindered. In clays, however, practically no infiltration takes place, and water and other liquid substances enter watercourses as runoff. Although the capacity of soils to retain water differs from their capacity to retain harmful substances (Table 3), the classification based on water-retention capacity provides us with a gauge by which to measure differences between soils.

To assess water-retention capacity we need geological interpretation as well as data on Quaternary deposits. Because of the way overburden is formed, impermeable soil strata are nearly always underlain by permeable soils, till or sorted sand and gravel. At the margins of permeable surficial deposits, a permeable deposit of fine sand, sand and gravel has commonly been deposited by the action of waves on impermeable clay and silt strata. In eskers, for instance, the soil strata are in hydraulic connection with each other, and one continuous aquifer is formed. As eskers make excellent foundations for roads, railways and urban buildings, environmentally harmful human activity has concentrated on what are geologically the most problematic areas. In future, then, hazardous operations should not be located in the risk areas marked on the map. If this is unavoidable, there are various technical measures for protecting and isolating them from aquifers. Geotextiles are effective but very expensive. The most cost effective is to use the impermeable soils — clay and fines-rich till — readily available in the Iisalmi area (green areas on the map).

## 7.2 Fracture zones in bedrock

Zones of weakness in bedrock — open fractures — conduct water and harmful substances for long distances. Fractures act like a drain, collecting water from a network of fractures over large areas and from the overburden. Elsewhere in Finland harmful substances are known to have travelled for tens of kilometres along bedrock fracture zones without visible manifestation. Under geologically favourable conditions these substances have emerged in a groundwater spring or downstream water course.

Wells drilled in bedrock in aquifers downstream

from landfills, scrap yards, industrial plants, sawmills, sewage-treatment plants and liquid manure plants are usually in a risk zone. If harmful substances are permitted to flow freely into bedrock fractures for decades, the bedrock groundwater reserves will eventually be polluted and rendered useless for a long time to come. Certain weakness zones extend for many kilometres down through the bedrock plate. It is known that some of the NW-SE trending bedrock fractures in the Ladoga-Bothnian Bay zone, which skirt the Iisalmi area, are deep fractures.

## 7.3 Scenic beauty

Special attention is paid to landscape values when planning land use and granting permits for the extraction of mineral resources. Many construction and raw material extraction projects have recently been prevented under the provisions of the 1991 Environmental Permit Procedures Act. Previously, many a beautiful esker landscape has been ruined by thoughtless extraction activities. A well designed and correctly aligned road can emphasize the outlines of the landscape, offering travellers viewpoints from which to enjoy the beauty around them. The environmental impact map and other thematic maps illustrate the geological structures that dominate the landscape. Topographically varied uplands, eskers, gently slop-

ing cultivated lake shores and sounds are all environmentally valuable yet highly vulnerable landscapes.

The Iisalmi district with its esker islands and the western area of hummocky moraines are geological entities characteristic of the Iisalmi landscape, where the outlines of landforms have been modified by human activity, agriculture and urban building (Fig. 13). More enduring are valleys and wooded and paludified plains. Marked on the map are various areas protected by law and also valuable areas listed by the town of Iisalmi. Also marked on the map are important aquifers and sites where quarrying etc., requires a permit under the Act on Extractable Land Resources.

Fig. 13. The area of hummocky moraines in the northern part of Iisalmi. Photo Kai Jägerholm.

## 7.4   Land, human beings and health

Liquid spills have recently contaminated land in a number of dangerous incidents, e.g. the breakage of a gasoline tank at a service station, a leak of sulphuric acid in a railway yard and the cracking of a wastewater pipe in an aquifer. Harmful chemicals entering the soil pose a health hazard, unless their circulation in soil is understood and controlled. Most insidious are the cases in which a harmful substance has been leaking into the soil and hence entering the natural cycle for a long time, without having been caused by a visible accident. High fluorine concentrations in groundwater and levels of radon above the statutory limits in buildings are examples of natural health risks caused by particular elements.

Radon does not cause risk in the Iisalmi area. Moreover, the uranium content of bedrock and soil is low. Radon contents in houses in Iisalmi are below the normative value of 200 Bq/m$^3$. The mean content in the Iisalmi area is 105 Bq/m$^3$ and the mean in Finland is 145 Bq/m$^3$ (Voutilainen 1994).

According to a recent study, arsenic exposure of population using arsenic-bearing drilled well water in the southwest of Finland was found to be at the same level as in Taiwan where several cancer types correlate dose dependently with the arsenic content of drinking water (Kurttio et al. 1995). As an outcome of the former study it was recommended that the the wells containing arsenic should not be used for drinking water.

At one site, large amounts of chlorophenole were found to have entered the groundwater and a local lake through the soil from a sawmill (Nysten 1994). The chlorophenole exposure caused by the water and fish food has increased the risk of local people developing certain types of cancer (The Finnish Medical Association 1993). Although only a small proportion of the population has been exposed, the health risk is serious and demonstrates that similar environmental accidents could occur elsewhere in Finland too. Statutory maximum limits have been imposed on the concentrations of harmful substances permitted in potable water (Anon 1992, 1994). In some cases, however, the contaminating substances have been compounds which are not often analysed in the routine monitoring of raw water.

The best way to avoid the health risks posed by environmental disasters is to anticipate and prevent hazards at the planning stage. The chemical behaviour, impact and decomposition of many substances in the ground are still not fully understood, but geological information can at least help us to delineate their migration routes. The environmental impact map is one of the tools that planners can use in seeking to prevent environmental health risks.

# 8   INFILTRATION MAP

*Osmo Koivistoinen and Jouko Saarelainen*

**The infiltration map is a source of basic information on the infiltration capacity of the soil (Fig. 14). The map can be used in planning household infiltration fields for waste water in rural areas. With the aid of the soil infiltration classification, supervisory authorities can issue more detailed directions for the treatment of waste water in soil.**

In rural areas, household waste waters cannot always be directed into the main sewerage. Therefore, in a treatment system developed for a single household or only a few households, the waste water is discharged either to a trench or into the soil via two or three sedimentation wells.

The purification capacity of sedimentation wells is not very high, as about 20% of the nutrients in the waste water remain in the wells. Moreover, the water discharged via the wells gives off an unpleasant smell when it enters the trench, and surficial waters are polluted. To prevent this pollution, it is recommended that waste waters should be discharged into the soil via a set of infiltration trenches or that a soil filter should be built. If constructed

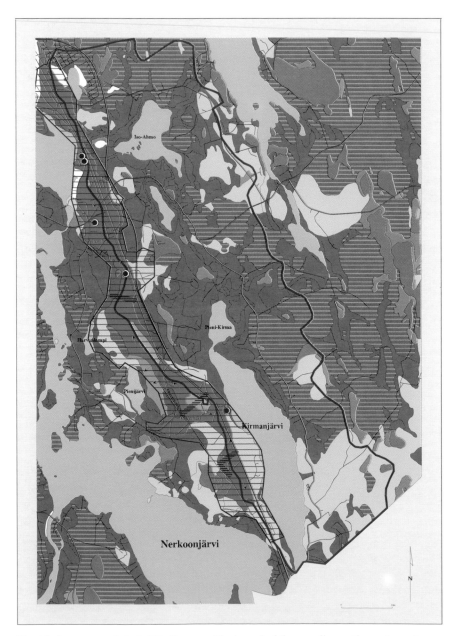

Fig. 14. An excerpt of the infiltration map (the legend of the map lies on the next page).

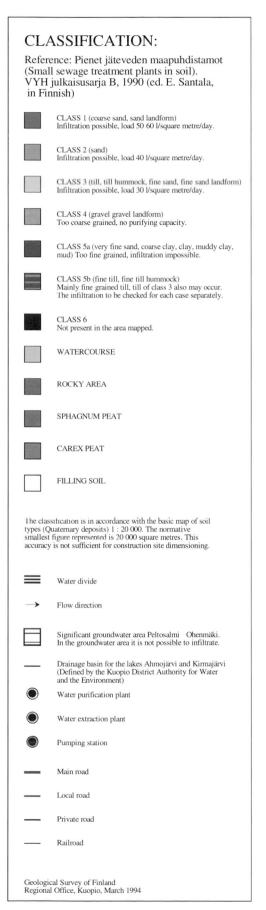

CLASSIFICATION:

Reference: Pienet jäteveden maapuhdistamot
(Small sewage treatment plants in soil).
VYH julkaisusarja B, 1990 (ed. E. Santala,
in Finnish)

CLASS 1 (coarse sand, sand landform)
Infiltration possible, load 50 60 l/square metre/day.

CLASS 2 (sand)
Infiltration possible, load 40 l/square metre/day.

CLASS 3 (till, till hummock, fine sand, fine sand landform)
Infiltration possible, load 30 l/square metre/day.

CLASS 4 (gravel gravel landform)
Too coarse grained, no purifying capacity.

CLASS 5a (very fine sand, coarse clay, clay, muddy clay,
mud) Too fine grained, infiltration impossible.

CLASS 5b (fine till, fine till hummock)
Mainly fine grained till, till of class 3 also may occur.
The infiltration to be checked for each case separately.

CLASS 6
Not present in the area mapped.

WATERCOURSE

ROCKY AREA

SPHAGNUM PEAT

CAREX PEAT

FILLING SOIL

The classification is in accordance with the basic map of soil
types (Quaternary deposits) 1 : 20 000. The normative
smallest figure represented is 20 000 square metres. This
accuracy is not sufficient for construction site dimensioning.

Water divide

Flow direction

Significant groundwater area Peltosalmi Ohenmäki.
In the groundwater area it is not possible to infiltrate.

Drainage basin for the lakes Ahmojärvi and Kirmajärvi
(Defined by the Kuopio District Authority for Water
and the Environment)

Water purification plant

Water extraction plant

Pumping station

Main road

Local road

Private road

Railroad

Geological Survey of Finland
Regional Office, Kuopio, March 1994

(The legend for the map in Fig. 14 on the previous page)

properly, infiltration trenches clean waste water very effectively, removing 65–95% of all harmful substances except nitrogen, which is reduced by only 20–40%. Purification is also excellent with soil filters.

Plans for treating waste waters in soil should take account of the capacity of the soil to infiltrate water, the risk of groundwater contamination (wells, water intake plants and important aquifers) and settlement in the area. In a densely built-up area the decision taken by one household may affect the ability of neighbours to arrange their water supply.

In Iisalmi, the authorities inspect each property on a new building site separately when processing the application for permission to build lavatories. During these inspections, builders are advised to take into consideration other houses being built in the area. The risk of contamination to nearby wells is also assessed. The guideline in permit decisions is that waste water should be discharged into the soil via two sedimentation wells using infiltration or soil filtering techniques.

Detailed information on the soil of such areas has seldom been available. Consequently, builders have dimensioned infiltration trenches on the basis of rather general specifications. The soil infiltration map will enable more detailed instructions to be given for the soil treatment of waste water and, if necessary, will encourage builders to commission comprehensive soil studies.

The capacity of the soil to take up household waste water depends on many factors, such as the grain size and water content of soils, the groundwater level and the compactness of the soil. The infiltration map is based mainly on the grain-size distribution of soils; the effects of groundwater level and soil compactness were omitted. It is imperative when estimating the local infiltration capacity to check that the groundwater level is deep enough, that is, at least 1 m beneath the infiltration surface.

The infiltration classification of soil is given by National Board of Waters and the Environment (Santala 1990). Soils are grouped into six classes by grain-size distribution (Table 4). An estimate of infiltration capacity and a recommended value for soil loads are given for each class. In class 1, infiltration is possible and the load can be 50–60 l/m$^3$ per day. In class 2, infiltration is possible but the load should not exceed 40 l/m$^3$ per day. In class 3, infiltration is also possible but the load should not exceed 30 l/m$^3$ per day. In class 4, infiltration is intense but the soil is too coarse-grained for the purification to be sufficient. In class 5, the soil is too fine-grained for infiltration and in class 6, fine-grained soils lower the infiltration capacity, and coarse-grained soils the purification capacity (Table 4).

Table 4. Soil grain-size classification and estimation of infiltration capacity by grain-size distribution (Santala 1990).

| Geo | Clay | Silt | Sand | Gravel |
|-----|------|------|------|--------|

| CLASS | AREA OF GRAINSIZE | INTFILRATION | LOAD / 1/m² / d |
|-------|-------------------|--------------|------------------|
| 1 | A | possible | 50 - 60 or > 60 |
| 2 | A and partly B | possible | maximum 40 |
| 3 | B and partly A | possible | maximum 30 |
| 4 | A and partly A in right | too coarse | -------------- |
| 5 | B and partly B in left | too finegrained | -------------- |
| 6 | outside A and B | too coarse and too finegrained | -------------- |

A thematic map of the infiltration capacity of soil has been produced for the studied catchment area on the basis of mapping data on Quaternary deposits and a geological interpretation (Fig. 14). According to the map of Quaternary deposits, the most common soil type in the catchment area (outlined in purple) is till. Its abundance is highest in the eastern, southeastern and northern parts of the area. In the west, the area is bordered by the Peltosalmi-Ohenmäki esker chain, which is an important aquifer and so unsuitable for wastewater infiltration. On the shores of watercourses the soil is mainly fine sand, clay and clayey gyttja.

Most of the area belongs to class 5 and is thus unsuitable for infiltration. In these areas the soils are either too fine-grained or too water-saturated for waste water infiltration. The till is mainly a fines-rich type, containing fines and clay in such abundance that it, too, is not suitable for infiltration. Southeast of Kirmajärvi, silty and sandy tills predominate. The boundary between silty and sandy tills, on the one hand, and fines-rich till, on the other, is not sharp. The patterns of fines-rich tills on the map of Quaternary deposits and those of silty and sandy tills indicate areas in which either of these till types predominates. The area of fines-rich tills may include small patches of silty and sandy tills with a high enough infiltration capacity. For the assessment of the infiltration capacity, the local till type must be checked separately. Therefore, class 5b has been used here.

According to the infiltration classification based on the map of Quaternary deposits, there are no class 1 infiltration areas in the Ahmojärvi-Kirmajärvi catchment, if the important Peltosalmi-Ohenmäki esker aquifer is excluded. Sandy areas (green on the map) and till and fine sand areas (pale green) are the best infiltration areas; they are most common in the southeastern part of the catchment. Peat and rocky areas were excluded from the assessment. Waste water entering bedrock joints and shears may migrate for long distances, e.g. to an aquifer. Infiltration should, therefore, not be carried out in shallow overburden covering fractured bedrock.

# 9  DISCUSSION AND CONCLUSIONS

*Maria Nikkarinen*

A scale of 1:50,000 was chosen for the maps because the authorities in the town of Iisalmi needed maps that would be of assistance in general planning over the entire municipal area. Descriptions at the regional planning level to a scale of 1:200,000 were already available, and also general plans for part of the area at 1:20,000. In addition, detailed geological mapping at the partial town plan scale of 1:4,000 had been carried out in the direction of proposed urban growth. The accurate location of buildings and definition of roads and railways always requires detailed geotechnical mapping on a large scale and large numbers of measurements and cores.

Scale and accuracy of the initial data together form the major factor which limits the usefulness of maps and sets of data in digital form. The great advantage of material of this kind lies in the potential for combining datasets to create a wide variety of thematic maps from the same basic material.

Groundwater is one of the most vital natural resources in Finland, and local authorities attempt wherever possible to take their water supplies from geological formations, eskers or bedrock fractures that contain pure groundwater. Even so, about 50% of the water used for public water supplies in Finland is still obtained from lakes or rivers, where in its natural state it characteristically contains large amounts of humus, which has to be removed by filtering and chlorination. The chemical treatment of water supplies naturally detracts from water quality and taste and implies the addition of potential carcinogens.

The water supply map and soil and groundwater vulnerability map are based to a great extent on the same material, processed according to the topic concerned in each case. Although the data on natural heavy metal concentrations are derived from an extensive programme of general geochemical mapping, no concentrations were discovered in the Iisalmi area that exceed the normative values, so that no restrictions would need to be placed on land use from this point of view. Similarly, the heavy metal content of the soil has not had any detrimental effect on the quality of well water. The major environmental problem in the area concerned here is that the urban agglomeration and the main roads and railway are located in the principal areas of groundwater formation, which are therefore in danger of becoming polluted by human agency. The intensive agriculture practised in the area, the emphasis placed on animal husbandry and the custom of fertilizing the fields in areas with clay and fine till soils with slurry points increase the nutrient loads on the rivers and lakes, while the ditching of mires and paludified forests is causing much leaching of nutrients from the fine till and humus from the peatlands into the waterways. Industrial building and long-distance transport of airborne pollutants do not at present pose any serious threat to the local environment, and the surficial deposits in the area are stable and the lakes and river not greatly susceptible to flooding, so that the risk of geological hazards is low. Furthermore, the quality of bedrock and soil does not cause radon risk; even though one high radiation anomaly was found in the airborne gamma radiation map. In follow-up studies of this anomaly it was noticed that is originates from the coating of a tennis court. Now the coating has been changed.

The collection of thematic maps presented here is intended as an example of the development work being carried out at GSF and does not yet represent a standard product available to meet the needs of every local or municipal council in Finland. GIS is a good tool for combining and analysing geological and other information intended for use in developmental environmental planning. In the long term it can be expected that digital geological information will be used interactively in land-use planning (Ryghaug 1996). Digital basic datasets can be accessed from the GSF directly as export files or through joint use of the Finnish spatial information system. Thematic maps can be produced for municipalities with a sufficiently comprehensive and wide-ranging coverage of geological data.

After producing the set of thematic maps, many follow-up projects have been established in the area. The map of natural resources gave a positive indication of exploitable geological materials in the area. In the recent investigations seven deposits of exploitable rocks (dolerite, montzonite and granite) were found. Now the municipalities of Economic Region of Nother-Savo have also decided to order a detailed investigation of exploitable sediments and soils. Kuopio University has started studies on the environmental impacts of harmful fluids in various types of soil.

Geoscientific environmental mapping meets the current requirements of both local authorities and central government and the GSF sees its task as being able to provide the consultancy services and basic geological information necessary for the assessment of natural resources, nature conservation, environmental studies, the evaluation of building plans and their impacts, land-use planning and new applications such as medical geology. The aim is to achieve sustainable development in human activities in the geo-environment and the most economical use of the abailable geological raw materials.

## 10 ACKNOWLEDGEMENTS

The authors wish to thank Osmo Koivistoinen, Jukka Virtanen and Jorma Väänänen (Iisalmi) for excellent teamwork during the project and Kai Jägerholm for taking the photos. We are grateful for Jouko Pennanen (The Federation of Northern Savo Economic Region) for being the encourager and inspirator to cooperation. Pekka Kallio, Per Ryghaug, Olle Selinus and Reijo Salminen critically read the manuscript and gave valuable comments. Gillian Häkli translated the manuscript into English.

## REFERENCES

**Anon 1992.** WHO Guidlines for Drinking-Water Quality, Volume 2: Health Criteria and other Supporting Information, Chapter 2: Chemical aspects.

**Anon 1994.** Sosiaali- ja terveysministeriön päätös talousveden laatuvaatimuksista ja valvontatutkimuksista 21.1.1994. nro 74, 246–254.

**ESRI 1992.** Understanding GIS. The Arc/Info Method. Redlands, USA: Environmental systems research institute, Inc. 549 p.

**Hyyppä, J. 1984.** Pohjaveden kemiallinen koostumus Suomen kallioperässä. Geologian tutkimuskeskus, ydinjätteiden sijoitustutkimukset. Voimayhtiöiden ydinjätetoimikunta (YJT), raportti YJT-84-10. 69 p.

**Jeltsch, U. 1990.** Saastuneiden maa-alueiden kunnostus. English summary: Remediation of contaminated soil. National Board of Waters and the Environment. Publications of the Water and Environment Administration — series A 44. 178 p.

**Koljonen, T. (ed.) 1992.** Suomen geokemian atlas, osa 2: Moreeni. The Geochemical Atlas of Finland, Part 2: Till. Espoo: Geological Survey of Finland. 218 p.

**Kukkonen, E. & Sahala, L. (eds.) 1988.** Iisalmen alueen maaperä. Summary: Quaternary deposits in the Iisalmi area. Geological map of Finland 1 : 100 000, Explanation to the maps of Quaternary deposits, Sheet 3341. Espoo: Geological Survey of Finland. 45 p.

**Kurttio, P., Sandström, H. & Pekkanen J. 1995.** Exposure to arsenic from drinking water in Finland. In: Saski, E. & Saarinen, T. (eds.) Proseedings. Second Finnish Conference of Environmental Sciences. Helsinki: Finnish Society for Environmental Sciences, 113–116.

**Lahermo, P., Ilmasti, M., Juntunen, R. & Taka, M. 1990.** The hydrogeochemical mapping of Finnish groundwater, The Geochemical Atlas of Finland, Part 1. Espoo: Geological Survey of Finland. 66 p.

**Lamminen, S. 1995.** Water-rock interaction in different rock environments. Geological Survey of Finland. Nuclear Waste Disposal Research. Report YST. 91. 60 p.

**Lappalainen, E & Hänninen, P. 1993.** Suomen turvevarat. Summary: The peat reserves of Finland. Geological Survey of Finland, Report of Investigation 117. 118 p.

**Ministry of Social and Health affairs 1991.** Sosiaali ja terveyshallinnon yleiskirje n.o 1977 15.2.1991. Talousveden terveydellisen laadun valvonta. Health criteria of drinking water.

**Niskavaara, H. 1995.** A comprehensive scheme of analysis for soils, sediments, humus and plant samples using inductively coupled plasma atomic emission spectrometry (ICP-AES). In: Autio, S. (ed.) Geological Survey of Finland, Current Research 1993–1994. Geological Survey of Finland, Special Paper 20, 167–175.

**Nysten, T. 1994.** Mathematical modelling of groundwater pollution in a small heterogenous aquifer at Kärkölä, southern Finland. Publications of the water and environmental research institute 15. 75 p.

**Paavola, J. 1991.** Iisalmen kartta-alueen kallioperä. Summary: Pre-Quaternary rocks of the Iisalmi map-sheet area. Geological map of Finland 1 : 100 000, Explanation to the maps of Pre-Quaternary rocks, Sheet 3341. Espoo: Geological Survey of Finland. 44 p.

**Peuquet, D. 1991.** Methods for structuring digital cartographic data in a personal computer environment. In: Taylor, D. (ed.) Geographic Information systems, The Microcomputer and Modern Cartography. Oxford: Pergamon Press. 251 p.

**Piispanen, R. & Nykyri, T. 1996.** Black schists as environmental threats. The 22nd Nordic Geological Winter meeting. Abstracts. Åbo: Åbo Akademi. 157 p.

**Puolanne, J., Pyy, O. & Jeltsch, U. 1994.** Saastuneet maa-alueet ja niiden käsittely Suomessa Saastuneiden maa-alueiden selvitys ja kunnostusprojekti; loppuraportti. Contaminated soil site survey and remediation project, Final report, Memorandum 5. Ministry of the Environment, Department for environmental projection. Helsinki: Painatuskeskus. 218 p.

**Räisänen, M. L., Tenhola, M. & Mäkinen, J. 1992.** Relationship between mineralogy and physico-chemical properties of till in central Finland. Bulletin of the Geological Society of Finland 64 (1), 35–58.

**Räisänen, M. L. 1989.** Mineraalimaan happamoituminen eräillä koealoilla teollisuuden lähiympäristössä ja tausta-alueilla Suomessa. Summary: The acidification of podzolized mineral soils in background areas and near industrial areas in Finland. Geological Survey of Finland, Report of Investigation 91. 74 p.

**Romu, M. 1978.** Iisalmen alueen kvartäärisavista ja niiden tiiliteknisistä ominaisuuksista. Quaternary clays and their geotecnical properties in Iisalmi area (in Finnish). University of Turku, Deparment of Quaternary geology, Publication 37. 34 p.

**Ryghaug, P. 1996.** The use of digital geological information in local planning and administration. A case study from the minicipality of Inderøy, Nord-Trøndelad. In: Neeb, P. R. (ed.) Geological Survey of Finland, Special Paper 22, 39–65 (this volume).

**Saarelainen, J. 1995.** Maaperän yleispiirteet Iisalmen alueella. General overwiev of soil in Iisalmi. In: Nikkarinen, M. (ed.) Geological information for municipal planning Thematic maps of Iisalmi (in Finnish). Geological Survey of Finland, Guide 39, 10–11.

**Salminen, R. (ed.) 1996.** Alueellinen geokemiallinen kartoitus Suomessa vuosina 1982–1994. Summary: Regional Geochemical Mapping in Finland in 1982–1994. Geological Survey of Finland, Report of Investigation 130. 47 p.

**Santala, E. (ed.) 1990.** Pienet jäteveden puhdistamot (Small soil-purification plants for wastewater.) Vesi- ja ympäristöhallituksen julkaisusarja B. 117 p.

**The Finnish Medical Association 1993.** Terveellinen ym-

päristö — ympäristötyöryhmän raportti. Healthy environment — report made by environmental group. Suomen Lääkäriliiton julkaisusarja 1993: 1. 49 p.

**Tikkanen, J. & Niemelä, J. 1975.** Soravarojen arviointi Inventation of gravel resources (in Finnish). TVL:n Kuopion piirin länsiosissa. Geological Survey of Finland, Quaternary department, report 13.3. 116 p.

**Voutilainen, A. 1994.** Asuntojen radonmittaukset. Iisalmi ja Vieremä. Säteilyturvakeskus Tutkimusselostus 6.5.1994. Radon measurements of houses in the Iisalmi and Vieremä areas. Finnish Centre for Radiation and Nuclear Safety, unpublished report. 10 p.

Geological information for environmental and land-use planning
in the Mid-Norden region
Edited by Peer-Richard Neeb
Geological Survey of Finland, Special Paper 22, 39–65, 1996.

# THE USE OF DIGITAL GEOLOGICAL INFORMATION IN LOCAL PLANNING AND ADMINISTRATION

## A case study from the municipality of Inderøy, Nord-Trøndelag, Norway

by

Per Ryghaug

**Ryghaug, Per 1996.** The use of digital geological information in local planning and administration. A case study from the municipality of Inderøy, Nord-Trøndelag, Norway. *Geological Survey of Finland, Special Paper 22*, 39–65, 22 figures.

Society is developing at an ever-increasing pace, and pressure on built-up areas, resources and the natural environment is growing. Continually changing land use requires solutions that can be applied immediately to any land-use conflicts that arise, and contribute to greater predictability regarding the consequences of our decisions. To achieve this, all relevant information must be readily available and kept up-to-date.

Information technology makes this possible. Geological information is often not included in this process owing to lack of availability or understanding. As a consequence of this the Geological Survey of Norway (NGU) is now transferring its knowledge about the country's bedrock, surficial deposits and groundwater into a geographical information system (GIS). GIS is being extensively employed by public institutions and local administrations, and digitised datasets are now widely available. Many political appraisals and decisions will within a few years be based on GIS solutions.

The key to any successful GIS solution, however, is the data. Using examples from a single local authority (Inderøy, in the county of Nord-Trøndelag), we will show how digital geological information helps to provide an overview of the natural resources of a municipality, documenting the occurrence of mineral deposits, building materials and groundwater potential. Focus is placed on how geological factors can help to significantly reduce costs when effluent from sparsely populated areas has to be dealt with. Appropriate presentation and use of data, e.g. from the mapping of landslide risks (areas containing quick clay), will reduce the risk of future landslides. The value of earth science conservation areas for the tourist industry, and geological information in the contexts of pollution and the environment, are also presented.

The incorporation of GIS in the decision-making process will improve land-use and resource management, if the information is complete, accurate and relevant. When geological information is combined in this way with land-use data from the municipal plan or other relevant information (waste disposals, business data, property boundaries, cultural relics and environmental data), the way is opened for many opportunities for geographical search, area statistics, area classification, and the analysis of land-use conflicts and presentation. It will be easier to document changes in land use within the municipality and to follow up the results in the future.

Key words (GeoRef Thesaurus, AGI): geologic maps, numerical maps, thematic maps, geographic information systems, mineral resources, ground water, environmental geology, land use, planning, Inderøy, Norway

*Per Ryghaug, Geological Survey of Norway*
*Box 3006 - Lade, N-7002 Trondheim,*
*NORWAY*

*E-mail: per.ryghaug@ngu.no*

# CONTENTS

# 1   INTRODUCTION

A primary objective with regard to development in Norway between now and the year 2000 is that it shall be based on the concept of sustainable development. The pollution of ground, water, sea and air must therefore be avoided, and ecologically acceptable utilisation of natural resources must be ensured. Geological factors are the very foundation of our environment and of the management of our resources and land. They influence our everyday lives, even though we may not be aware of it. Settlement patterns, development of rural communities, communications, economic potential in the mineral-based industry, the food and drink industry, water quality, biological diversity and tourism are from the outset heavily influenced by geological factors. Knowledge of the natural background values of environmental toxins is also vital in order to prove prospective man-made pollution. This provides us with opportunities for preventing development resulting in environmental loads that exceed the toleration limits set by nature. Notwithstanding, geology remains practically unmentioned in county and municipal land-use planning in Norway, and in action plans that have followed it.

Substantial costs are imposed on society when wrong decisions are taken at regional or local levels in the land-use and resource planning and management sectors. When this occurs, the reason is often that the basis for decision-making is not good enough. Relevant information is not available in a form that enables it to be taken into consideration during the planning and assessment stages. Every day, decisions are taken which have a bearing on the environment or the natural resources without geological information being taken into consideration.

"Geology for society" is the NGU slogan, and a set of aims has recently been drawn up which shows the fields and target groups upon which NGU is focusing (Fig. 1). The four primary objectives show that efforts are being concentrated on

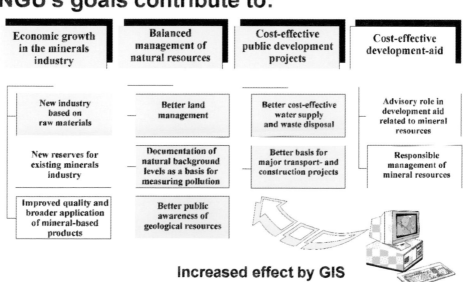

Fig. 1. NGU's target structure, with four primary goals ranked from left to right.

helping to increase value creation in mineral-based industry, by finding new deposits. The public sector is another important target area. Natural resources must be managed correctly and efforts will be centred on helping to save money on public-sector development projects.

NGU has so far largely presented its data in the form of reports, publications and map series. Data, however, are not synonymous with information. Christensen et al. (1991) defined information as data which, through de-coding and interpretative processes, express opinions that, on their part, can be looked upon as new knowledge. Thus, in order that digital geological data may be considered as information for local government, which often lacks special geological expertise, they must be transformed and customised to suit the user.

As figure 1 shows, the claim is made that the use of geographical information systems (GIS) will significantly improve the efficiency of this work. The aim of this article is to prove the validity of such a claim by giving examples of how digital geological information can be utilised in management on the local government level. By developing derived and customised information, which is quality assured through detailed documentation of metadata for the dataset and extensive use of quality parameters for every features, NGU is seeking to increase the use of geological information in land-use and resource planning at regional and local levels. A change from analogue to digital map production and the building-up of specialised databases have formed the foundation at NGU for the introduction of GIS and for enhanced customisation for the user. We are convinced that more active use of geological information will lead to better management of areas and resources, and ensure this sustainable development.

The interest for introducing GIS as part of a management system seems to be widespread in public-sector management circles, bringing geographical information into business. The system handles large volumes of data and by combining and multi-utilising different themes the cost-benefit effect is expected to reach 1:4 (Nordisk KVANTIF 1987). GIS paves the way for new and improved opportunities for revealing land-use conflicts at an early stage in the planning process relative to traditional paper maps, and its flexibility and functionality will make it a valuable access tool for enforcing correct land use (Ryghaug 1995a).

## 2  THE CASE STUDY AREA — INDERØY

To make the examples realistic, we are concentrating on data from one single municipality only, and have chosen Inderøy (Fig. 2) in the county of Nord-Trøndelag. It represents the western coastal

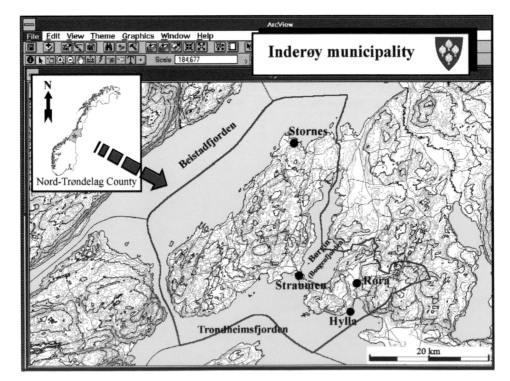

Fig. 2. Key maps showing the location of the municipality of Inderøy in Central Norway.

Fig. 3. Picture of parts of Inderøy municipality looking in a north-westerly direction. Hylla quarry is in the foreground and Staumen in the background. Photo by Reidulf Lyngstad.

flank of the Mid-Norden area, and with a surface area of 146 km² and 5816 inhabitants (1990), it is considered to be a small municipality. The population density, however, is the highest in the county (39.8 per km²). The population trend is positive, and in percentage terms its growth in population was the next highest in the county from 1980 to 1990. Inderøy is largely situated on a peninsula in the inner part of Trondheimsfjord and its landscape is typical for an agriculturally based rural municipality (Fig. 3) with a predominantly dispersed settlement pattern, but also includes a few relatively small, built-up centres. Its administrative centre is Sakshaug near Straumen (995 inhabitants). Other built-up areas, such as Røra and Hylla, are dealt with in this article. The local authority administration has so far not implemented GIS as a planning procedure.

## 2.1 Bedrock

The bedrock consists of metamorphosed volcanic and sedimentary rocks of assumed Cambrian to Early Ordovician age (i.e. between c. 540 and 470 million years old). Greenstone dominates in the north and greenstone and amphibolite in the east, whereas the southern and central parts are dominated by alternating beds of phyllite and shale (Fig. 4). A thick limestone horizon, which trends N-S adjacent to the greenstone in the east, is of special interest. The peninsula is traversed by a number of N-S trending joint sets and is bounded by several major NE-SW trending faults belonging to the Møre-Trøndelag Fault Zone. A summary of the bedrock geology of Norway can be found in the Guide to the Bedrock Geological Map of Norway (Sigmond 1985).

## 2.2 Surficial deposits

The cover of surficial deposits is for the most part thin. The location of Inderøy, on a peninsula separating the main part of Trondheimsfjord in the south from its northerly branch, Beitstadfjord, means that marine deposits dominate in addition to weathered bedrock (Fig. 5). Conditions for cultivation are therefore good. Thick occurrences of surficial deposits are scarce, but a large marginal moraine crosses the mouth of Børgin, an arm of Trondheimsfjord near Straumen. A source for a more detailed account of the distribution of surficial deposits in Norway and their mode of formation is "the Quaternary map of Norway" (Thoresen 1991).

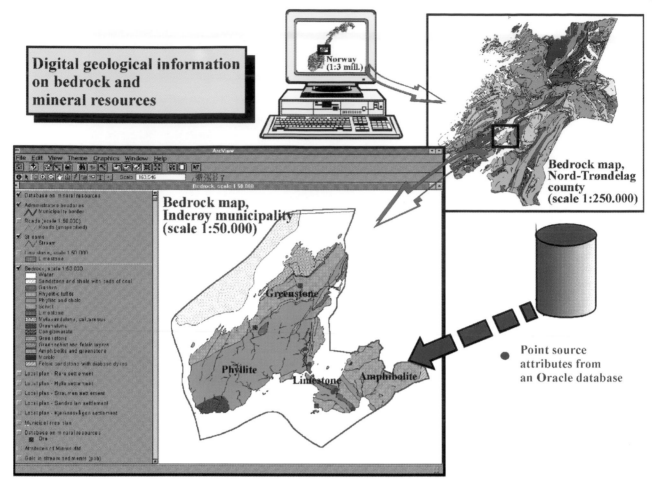

Fig. 4. Information about the bedrock is based on mapping and observations carried out on various scales, depending on whether they are intended for national, regional or local levels. Map data can be combined with information on attributes taken from NGU's databases. Active themes are identified by a tick on the icon in the legend to the left. The colour of the texture and background can be freely varied.

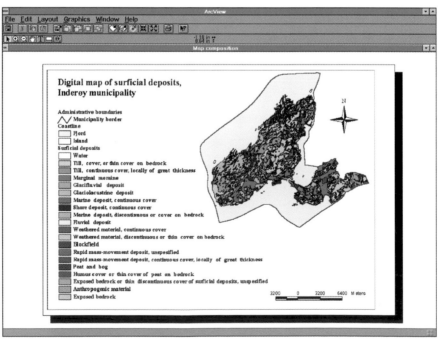

Fig. 5. Digital surficial deposit map for Inderøy as displayed on the screen using the ArcView layout program. The choice of colours for the types of surficial deposits in the legend follows the NGU standard for Quaternary maps.

# 3 GEOGRAPHICAL INFORMATION SYSTEM (GIS)

A geographical information system is a software system which handles the capture, processing, analysis, storage and presentation of information from specific locations. It is not the intention here to give a detailed explanation of how a GIS functions, or to describe the specificational requirements and organisational conditions that should apply. These aspects are adequately dealt with elsewhere (e.g. Burrough 1986, Bernhardsen 1992, ESRI 1992).

Like many other institutions, NGU has implemented GIS gradually. The first feeble attempts go back to 1989 when the principal need was for a tool that was suitable for comparison of raster and vector-based data in connection with ore prospecting. The building-up of digitised datasets, and of expertise, has now reached a stage where the need is seen to use the tool as a complete management system which will be able to administer all of NGU's data from collection to presentation. The need to develop standardised thematic code sets and quality parameters has also been recognised.

NGU has chosen Arc/Info® as its GIS tool. Arc/Info®, developed by ESRI (Environmental Systems Research Institute Inc.) is one of several such systems. It is a large and expensive system and still has a high user threshold. It is, nevertheless, not necessary to obtain the system to be able to use data which have Arc/Info format. User-friendliness has increased significantly following the development of low-cost Windows-based desktop GIS tools such as ArcView®, which simplifies the viewing and use of the data. ArcView has gradually developed into an adequate tool for the analysis and presentation of information relating to specific locations. The system supports a range of importing, exporting and printing formats, has spatial query based on look-up tables, analysis functions and good visualisation techniques. Most of the figures in this article have been produced using ArcView in combination with the graphic program CorelDraw™. Special importing functions in ArcView enable the inclusion of point source data with ordinary ASCII flat-file or dBase™ formats provided the table contains x and y coordinates.

A rapidly increasing number of public-sector management bodies and county and local government authorities have introduced GIS as an important element in their handling of data from specific locations. The Nord-Trøndelag county authority has reached an advanced stage in the task of establishing a digitised data foundation that can be used by everyone involved in managing resources and areas under the terms of the Planning and Building Act or sectoral acts. The county has begun using ArcView as a tool in administrative procedures, and several municipal authorities in the county are following its example.

# 4 DATA ARCHITECTURE

## 4.1 Data source

All geological data can be looked upon as specifically located data. The digital geological information will consist of geological themes derived from NGU's map series, linked to themes captured from the base map. These may, for example, be administrative boundaries, coastlines and river systems. The geological information has largely been recorded (mapped) in connection with a co-ordinated geological investigation programme for Nord-Trøndelag and Fosen funded by the Department of Industry and Energy and the two county authorities of Nord- and Sør-Trøndelag. In the course of a separate GIS project (1992–1995), digital geological information has been prepared for the whole of Nord-Trøndelag (Ryghaug 1992). Co-operation with another project, "GIS project for Steinkjer", funded by NTNF (Royal Norwegian Council for Scientific and Industrial Research) and the Nord-Trøndelag county authority, gave access to the digitised base map and the necessary contact with users. Active partners in this context have been the county geologist, the planning department, the reindeer husbandry office, the county curator and the county agricultural office.

### 4.1.1 Base map

During the cooperation project with the Nord-Trøndelag county authority a two-way free flow of digital data was practised, which meant that the resources of the individual partner could be concentrated on digital data capture of its own data. The essential digitised base map data were originally obtained from the Norwegian Mapping Authority, and made available to the partners after a significant quality improvement had been carried out by a consulting firm. It was decided to use a common data specification and naming convention. The thematic codes used on the base map follow a Norwegian standard format called SOSI (Statens kartverk 1995). All the locations are specified using one single grid system (UTM zone 32 and datum ED50).

### 4.1.2 Geological map series

The geological information is based on raw data from NGU's map series, i.e. bedrock maps and Quaternary maps on several scales. The degree of detail (or the scale) on the digital map must be customised for the use to which it is intended (Fig. 4).

The information on the bedrock geology in Inderøy (Fig. 4) is based on mapping on a 1:50,000 scale (D. Roberts, unpubl.). This is a part of a compiled digital bedrock map of Nord-Trøndelag and Fosen (Solli, unpubl.).

A surficial deposit map shows the distribution of various types of surficial deposits and their thickness (Fig. 5). The intention is that digital information on surficial deposits will be based on the most detailed information available. For Inderøy, the base map was assembled from data on six Quaternary maps of varying quality, age and scale (Fig. 6). Multicoloured maps on a scale of 1:20,000 covering the eastern part of Inderøy have been published (Sveian 1985a, 1985b, 1992, Sveian & Bjerkeli 1984), but the western part is only covered by a manuscript map on a scale of 1:50,000 (A. Reite, unpubl.). Material from a marginal zone between these two types of map had to be extracted from a multicoloured map printed on a scale of 1:50,000 (Sveian 1985c). A similar situation will exist irrespective of which municipality is considered.

Because the municipality of Inderøy covers a very small area and has relatively homogeneous geology, it is obviously impossible to demonstrate the full range of geological information here. Nonetheless, some principles and the demands that have to be stipulated regarding the quality of this kind of digital information can be illustrated.

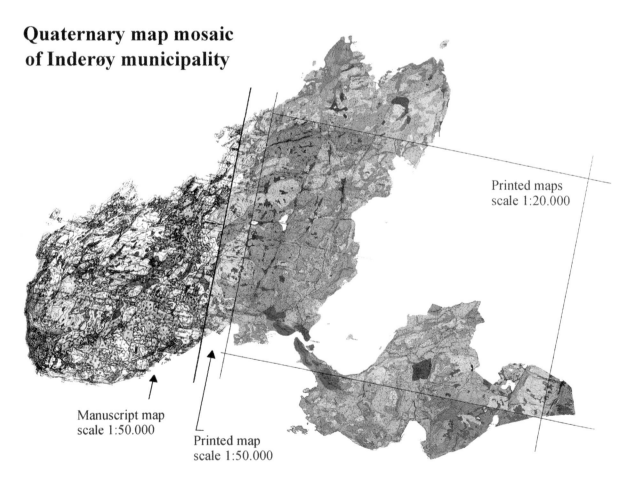

**Quaternary map mosaic of Inderøy municipality**

Printed maps
scale 1:20.000

Manuscript map
scale 1:50.000

Printed map
scale 1:50.000

Fig. 6. Map mosaic for Inderøy consisting of several different analogue surficial deposit maps on scales of 1:20,000 and 1:50,000. These maps form the basis for the digital surficial deposit map (Fig. 5).

### 4.1.3 Databases

NGU is responsible for developing and maintaining a national geological data bank. Its separate databases covering ores, industrial minerals, dimension stone, and sand, gravel and rock aggregates are important ingredients in this data bank. Long-known and newly-found occurrences of mineral deposits are included in these databases. These databases have been assembled using the Oracle database tool, and can be accessed through the GIS tool (Fig. 4). Information about NGU's publication series (Skrifter, now called Gråsteinen, Bulletin and Special Publications) and reports can be reached through a reference database. The reference database are accessible from our World Wide Web homepage on the Internet (http://www/ngu.no), and gradually all the others too.

## 4.2 Quality control

NGU's intention is that the ISO 9000 standard (a standard from the International Standardisation Organisation) will form the basis for the production of digitised information, and the policy for its distribution and storage. By stipulating international demands on quality leadership and quality system elements (cf. the quotation from ISO 9004), NGU wishes to ensure that the production:

- meets a defined requirement, area of use or objective
- satisfies the expectations of the client
- satisfies relevant standards and specifications
- satisfies statutory demands laid down by society
- is available at competitive prices.

The building-up of a file containing metadata (i.e. data about data) is an important element in this quality assurance. Metadata include a description of the content, aim, use and processing history of the dataset, as well as who has produced it, the contact person and how the information can be obtained. Not only an overview of the quality, positioning and thematic content must be given, but also their relevance.

The quality concept itself is relative. What is good quality for one user may be poor quality for another. A geological map database for a county or a municipality may be based on information taken from several kinds of maps on different scales, of different ages, and varying in degree of detail, etc. (Fig. 6). This places great demands on quality assurance. It must be possible to check the derivation of the data and their quality, and also to retain the information for subsequent updating. This is information that must be linked to each individual feature (lines, polygons and points) in the dataset, not only to descriptions given in separate metadata files or reports (Ryghaug 1995b). In this way it is possible to counter erroneous interpretations and misuse of information.

The viewing tool, ArcView®, permits inspection of the various parameters such as map scale, map identity, positional accuracy, medium character, measuring method, thematic accuracy, entry data, last update date and data references. In figure 7 it is easy to see from which map the surficial deposit boundaries derive by giving the lines different colours based on the map identification numbers. Additional quality parameters which are attached to the lines are shown in the table subwindow, and these can be inspected for each line by clicking the line to which the cursor on the screen is pointing.

## 4.3 Data capture and creation of themes

Foils for printing of maps, each one dealing with a separate theme, were scanned and vectorised using NGU's Intergraph® system. Preliminary maps (manuscript maps) were digitised with FYSAK, a software system made by the Norwegian Mapping Authority. All the vectors were transferred to Arc/Info to have themes and attributes allocated. It was realised at an early stage that standardised thematic codes needed to be worked out, though preliminary geological thematic codes were prepared for this purpose. Standardisation work in this field has now been initiated by NGU, and the first standard (material deposit extraction) has been published as part of version 2.2 of SOSI (Statens kartverk 1995).

One reason for geology being less used in a regional planning context is probably that the meaning of, and use for, such data are inadequately known or too difficult to understand. Some data have to undergo a customised inter-

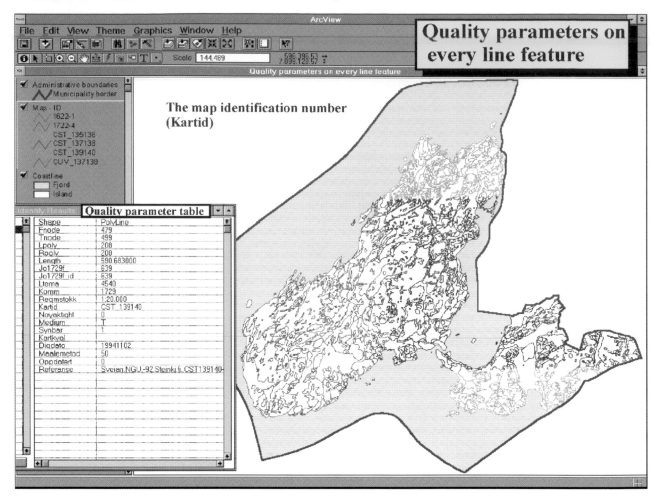

Fig. 7. As an important link in the quality assurance of the data, all the line segments have been equipped with quality parameters in the table of attributes. The figure shows how it is possible to determine from which map-sheet the line originates. If the left mouse button is clicked while the cursor is pointing at one of the lines, the table (in Norwegian) containing the processing history of the line is displayed on the screen.

pretative process to become more useful in land-use planning and resource management. The map in figure 5 shows how digital surficial deposit data can be presented on the screen (or on paper) in traditional colours from printed Quaternary maps. Based on the grain-size distribution, thickness, etc. of the types of surficial deposits, derived products can be developed that are more directly significant for the planning process (Fig. 8). The largest groundwater reservoirs are usually located in surficial deposits. Likewise, the ability of surficial deposits to filter and cleanse water can be exploited in connection with the increasing tendency to treat effluent. Resources of sand and gravel aggregates are obviously also an important parameter when the total significance of the surficial deposits is being clarified.

The potential can be extended further if the decision is taken to derive still more information from the surficial deposits by developing themes which illustrate suitability with regard to farming areas and construction of forestry roads, variations in ground conditions in connection with building sites or landslide risk, or load-carrying capacity to counter load damage (wheel tracks) in connection with unauthorised, off-road, motorised transport.

Similar thematic derivation is also possible in connection with bedrock data. The chemical weathering of rock types, i.e. an important factor in nature's own sensitivity against acidification (Fig. 18; see page 61), can be classified. The same applies to natural radioactivity in the bedrock, or the potential for economic deposits.

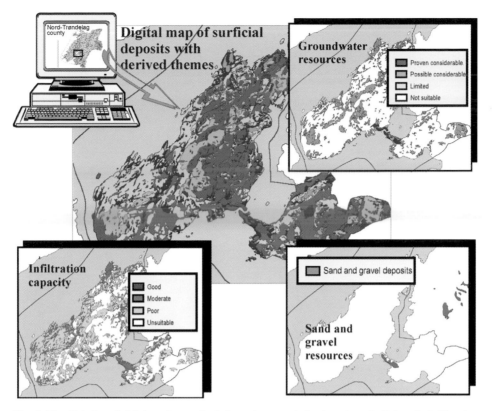

Fig. 8. The digital surficial deposit map for Inderøy has two derived products built into it (infiltration capacity and groundwater potential). These become independent map themes when activated. The areas of sand and gravel resources registered in NGU's aggregates database can also be displayed on maps.

# 5 APPLICATION OF GEOLOGICAL INFORMATION

## 5.1 Mineral resources

One definition of an ore is a rock in which one or more elements or minerals has been so richly concentrated that the rock has become of economic interest. In the case of dimension stone (incl. flagstone), it is the appearance of the rock and its ability to withstand wear and tear that make it interesting. For sand, gravel and crushed hard rock aggregates, all of which are important construction materials, their ability to withstand wear and tear and weathering, as well as their grain size, are important when assessing quality and area of use.

NGU has, as mentioned earlier, a complete, countrywide overview of occurrences of mineral deposits, i.e. ore deposits, dimension stones, industrial minerals and construction materials such as sand, gravel and rock aggregates in Norway stored in Oracle-based databases. These are being continuously expanded and maintained. In the rock-related databases, the occurrences are registered as points, with information on, e.g. type of mineralisation, size, manner of working, etc. When the theme has

been entered in ArcView (Fig. 9), all attributes concerning the theme are displayed on the screen when the locality is selected (clicked on).

In the municipality of Inderøy, three ore deposits, seven industrial mineral deposits and one dimension stone occurrence are registered in the NGU databases. The table in figure 9 shows that the limestone occurrence dominates. When a rock represents a possible mineral resource, emphasis is put on mapping its extent in as much detail as possible. If only regional mapping exists (small-scale mapping), this will, if possible, be supplemented by more detailed mapping (on scale 1:10,000 to 1:50,000). The limestone in figure 10 has been registered on aerial photographs on a scale of 1:30,000 and has been transferred to maps on a scale of 1:50,000. All the six limestone occurrences from the NGU database are linked to this rock unit. This limestone is the most important mineral occurrence in Inderøy.

The dimension stone occurrence that has been

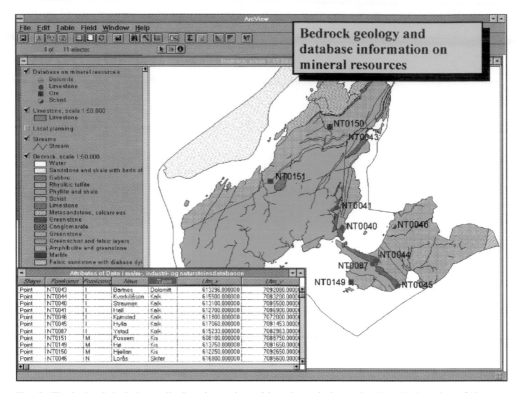

Fig. 9. The bedrock in Inderøy displayed together with a thematic layer showing the location of the ore, industrial mineral and dimension stone occurrences recorded in the respective NGU databases. The stream system theme has also been activated on the screen because this gives an indication of the joint sets present in the area. All tabular database information (in Norwegian) is available through the system.

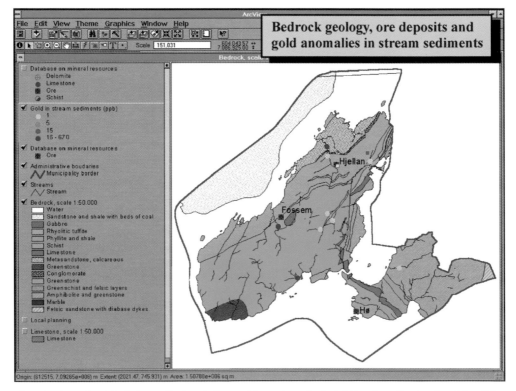

Fig. 10. The bedrock in Inderøy displayed along with ore deposits (sulphide mineralisations) and localities where stream sediments have been analysed for gold. The symbol for gold becomes redder the higher the gold concentration in the sediment (a sample from outside Inderøy is responsible for the maximum concentration of 670 ppb in the legend).

registered (Fig. 9) represents a small flagstone locality, without any economic interest.

None of the ore occurrences registered in Inderøy are of economic interest. All three represent thin sulphide mineralisations in greenstone (Fig. 10). In connection with regional studies of the content of gold in stream sediments in the county, a few gold anomalies were recorded in Inderøy (Fig. 10). The gold content, which in places has concentrations of 15–50 ppb (parts per billion), can be linked to similar anomalies on Ytterøy, where small amounts of gold have been found in thin alteration zones in thebedrock. In Inderøy the gold is not linked to the recorded sulphide mineralisations (Fig. 10), and it has not been possible to prove concentrations in bedrock or visible grains in stream sand. It is therefore difficult to exploit these registrations in connection with, for instance, tourism (gold panning).

Sand and gravel are among the most important construction materials in the country. Since such resources are not renewable and, nation-wide, represent a significant production value, the importance of managing them well is obvious. Every occurrence of this material throughout the country is registered in the NGU database for sand, gravel and rock aggregates (Neeb 1995). Altogether 8,790 sand and gravel deposits and 6,546

sand and gravel pits are registered. Analogue presentations of such deposits, in the form of sand and gravel resource maps and planning maps, have been prepared previously (Wolden & Erichsen 1990). However, when a geographical information system is applied to the database the usefulness of the data increases appreciably. Information about any working of the deposit, the average volume and suitability assessments for various forms of use for the area covered by the deposit are accessible through a spatial query. An evaluation of the suitability of the deposit is based on figures acquired by measurements and analyses at individual localities within the deposit, and the quality demands are based on international standards. The GIS-based spatial query and analysis functions result in assessments of land use, accessibility and ownership becoming more updated. This permits a far more strategic management of the resource than was previously possible. Combining such data with a digital road network, digital property maps database and requirement analyses, paves the way for improved transport planning, land redistribution transactions and analyses of land-use conflicts.

Even though the cover of surficial deposits is thin, the database records seven gravel deposits within the boundaries of Inderøy (Fig. 11). The

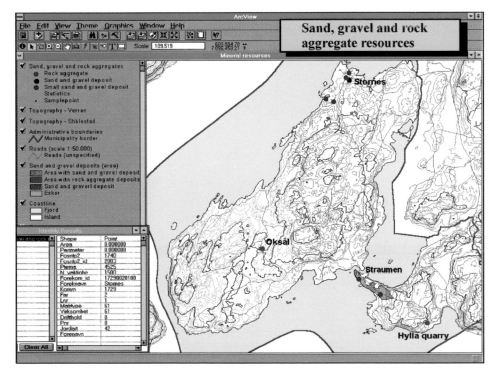

Fig. 11. Localities in Inderøy with deposits of sand, gravel and crushed hard rock aggregate. A deposit near Straumen that extends over a relatively large area is also shown (likewise in Fig. 8). The portion of the table shown displays some of the attributes (in Norwegian) that have been recorded for the deposits; it complies withthe thematic codes in the SOSI description used for extraction of mineral resources. Contours, the road network and municipal boundaries are also activated themes.

largest one is part of a large marginal moraine at Straumen, separating Børgin from the fjord. This feature locally contains sorted material. In addition, several small occurrences are found near Stornes in connection with shore deposits, scattered occurrences of which are found throughout Inderøy. Since these are seldom more than 2 metres thick, material is only extracted for local use. The table sub-window in figure 11 shows some of the information which the user can display when an occurrence on the map is selected.

Crushed hard rock aggregates are the most important building material in Norway (Neeb 1995). However, the bedrock in Inderøy does not include any rock which produces good quality aggregates for road construction or making concrete. Despite this, two rock aggregate occurrences are recorded in the database (Fig. 11). At Oksål, strongly fractured greywacke and phyllite are being used as rock aggregate in an occurrence which NGU has evaluated as being unsuitable for most purposes. Some limestone from the Hylla limestone quarry is also being used as aggregate, and the occurrence therefore also figures in the aggregate database.

## 5.2 Groundwater resources

It has been claimed that one million people in Norway, i.e. a quarter of the country's inhabitants, are daily drinking water that is too poor in quality (Ellingsen 1992). More than 80% of the nation's water supplies are based on surface water. In Nord-Trøndelag, supplies from several waterworks are still unsatisfactory. Firms engaged in the food and drink industry and tourism sectors will experience problems in fulfilling European Union standards on water quality if new and improved water supplies cannot be offered quickly. Because of the special qualities displayed by groundwater, the situation would be different if that source had been used more for supplying water. The costs involved in establishing an alternative water source usually come out in favour of groundwater (Ellingsen 1992). This concerns groundwater both from bedrock and surficial deposit sources, but the greatest potential lies in the latter.

The quality of the water supply in the municipality of Inderøy used to be poor, but the construction of a new purifying plant for the surface water source has improved the situation. Even with a predominantly thin cover of surficial deposits, Inderøy has certain possibilities for extracting groundwater from such sources. Figure 12 shows the potential for groundwater resources in Inderøy, based on information derived from the digital surficial deposits map (Fig. 5). On a groundwater resource map the initial automatic classification based on the type of surficial deposit is followed by the geologist adjusting this on the basis of detailed information available on the area (varying grain size, thickness, stratigraphy and location relative to rivers and lakes, etc.). Since the water supply in Inderøy is now satisfactory, this groundwater theme is primarily of interest in the event of reserve water resources being needed for scattered settlements. A possible occurrence will have to be proved by test drilling to obtain information on capacity and quality. NGU is now building up a well database containing such information. The local authority can gain access to a copy of this through the GIS tool, and later on through an Internet interface. Wells have been registered in Inderøy, both in bedrock and in surficial deposits (Fig. 12). In addition to their geographical location, the GIS provides access to the type of well, the well owner and the capacity and quality of the water. Information on water quality can also be presented graphically. If the groundwater information is combined with datasets showing existing waterworks, location relative to firms involved in the food and drink industry and tourism (which require better water quality), and possible sources of contamination (waste disposals, effluent systems, transportation routes for hazardous waste, or areas where intensive farming takes place), the opportunities for justifiable management of this important natural resource are enhanced. Conflict and risk maps can be prepared which, with the help of buffering techniques, will emphasise areas where the risk for contamination of the groundwater is greatest (Nikkarinen 1996).

## 5.3 Effluent clearance and waste disposal control

Modern society is continually changing our natural environment, and effluent and sewage still contaminate many Norwegian river systems and fjords. Untreated seepage from waste disposals may also threaten groundwater and river systems. In this context, it has been stated that a primary objective of the county plan is to preserve the environmental qualities of the Trondheimsfjord. The ever stricter de-

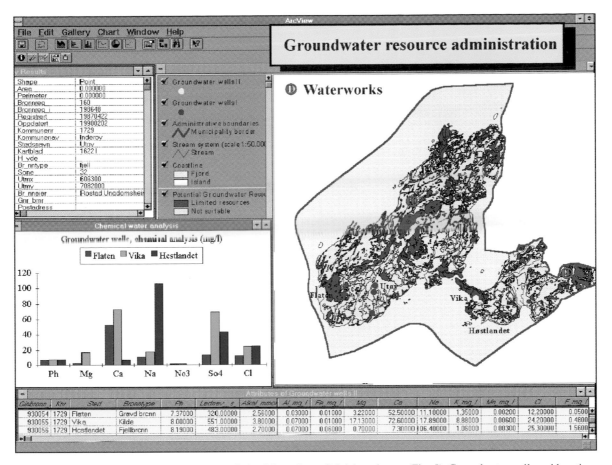

Fig. 12. Groundwater resource map for Inderøy derived from the surficial deposit map (Fig. 5). Groundwater wells and locations of existing waterworks are also shown. The portion of the table in the upper left shows some of the attributes recorded (in Norwegian). The table below shows that several types of well (bronntype in Norwegian) are involved. The water quality can also be displayed graphically. The map, table and graphic sub-windows are in interactive connection with each other. If one or more localities are activated on the map, this also has an automatic consequence for the table and the bar diagram.

mands now being placed on the cleansing of effluent and sewage from areas of scattered settlement will entail substantial public-sector investments. The National Pollution Control Authority (SFT) has also introduced more stringent environmental demands regarding waste disposal and incinerators.

It has been recognised for a long time that local authority effluent is responsible for large inputs of phosphorus and nitrogen to our rivers, lakes and coastal seas. It is therefore interesting to note that Inderøy was the first local authority in the country to take a political decision imposing on itself the demand to treat the effluent from all its settlements by the year 2000. Infiltration of effluent into suitable surficial deposits is an alternative to mini cleansing plants, and can give large economic gains. The surficial deposits act as a filter where the contaminants are retained and in part broken down whilst the water passes through and is cleansed. This is also an aspect to be aware of when the risk of polluted seepage from a waste disposals is being

assessed and counter measures are being introduced.

The ability of the surficial deposits to filter and cleanse effluent can in broad terms be classified on the basis of the type of surficial deposit shown on a map of such deposits (Fig. 5). Following the automatic classification, the geologist adjusts the classification results on the basis of available supplementary information in the same way as for the groundwater theme. The infiltration map for Inderøy (Fig. 13) gives an overview of the possibilities that are at hand for solving this self-imposed treatment of effluent with the aid of infiltration into the surficial deposits. GIS buffering techniques can be applied to insert safety zones along all the river systems and around groundwater wells. Even though Inderøy has few thick sand and gravel deposits, the small-scale map shows that it nevertheless seems feasible to construct small infiltration plants in shore deposits, sandy moraines and thick deposits of soil derived from rock weathering.

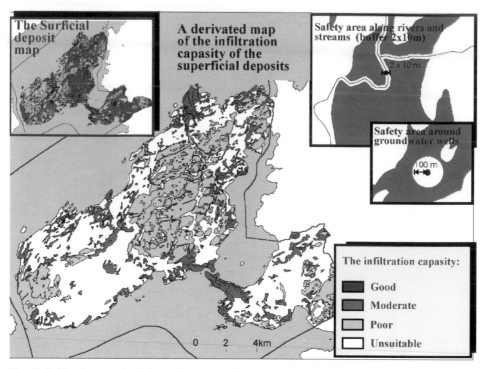

Fig. 13. Infiltration map for Inderøy, based on information derived from the surficial deposit map in the upper left sub-window. If desired, a buffer zone can be generated in the dataset, based on safety zones along water courses or around groundwater wells.

The decision to treat effluent entailed the division of Inderøy into three effluent zones (Fig. 14) where cleansing was to be carried out in zone 1 by 1994, zone 2 by 1997 and zone 3 by 2000. There was a need for more detailed and more specialised infiltration mapping to determine whether suitable masses are really present, and to find the most suitable location for an infiltration plant. Detailed investigations,

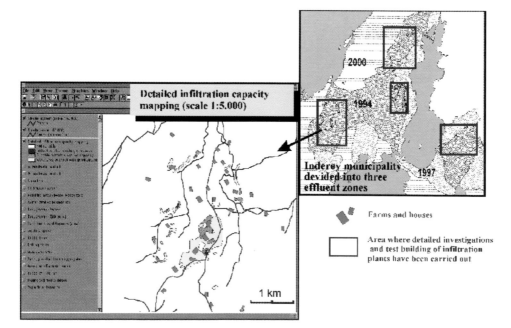

Fig. 14. On the right, the plan for effluent and sewage treatment in Inderøy is displayed, along with areas where NGU and Jordforsk have carried out more detailed investigations. One of these areas is zoomed (enlarged) to the left side of the figure, and settlements are also displayed here. The Fig. shows that suitable surficial deposits occur within a short distance of several of these settlements.

based on maps on a scale of 1:5000 and infiltration tests, were carried out in 1992–93 in four limited areas within zone 1 (Fig. 14). The results showed that it was possible to solve the effluent problem for up to 65% of the scattered settlements in these areas with the help of naturally based cleansing methods (Hilmo & Sveian 1993). Infiltration plants have since been constructed and tests show good results so far. Extrapolated for the whole of Inderøy, the costs estimation shows that the use of infiltration plants rather than traditional solutions would give a significant cost reduction.

This detailed mapping also made it possible to check how reliable the derived infiltration map was for providing an initial indication of the prospects for infiltration in the area. A test of the conformity between comparison detailed mapping and the derived infiltration map was carried out. The agreement proved to be generally good (Fig. 15), particularly taking into consideration the differences

in registration precision. The figure also shows how, with the help of Arc/Info, it is possible to access the infiltration theme within zone 1 alone, for thereafter to be able to calculate an area statistically showing the total area containing surficial deposits with a suitable infiltration capacity. The results show that 41% of the area within zone 1 can be expected to have such possibilities. Areas containing surficial deposits with infiltration potentials are often areas which are preferred as building ground. The fact that a larger proportion of settlements (65%) proved to have infiltration potentials following detailed mapping thus, was not unexpected. A derived infiltration map is therefore considered to be very useful when the plans and the costs of effluent cleansing are being assessed. The infiltration map is also of interest when evaluating suitable alternative localities in connection with waste disposals, and when assessing the risk of contaminated seepage water from existing disposals.

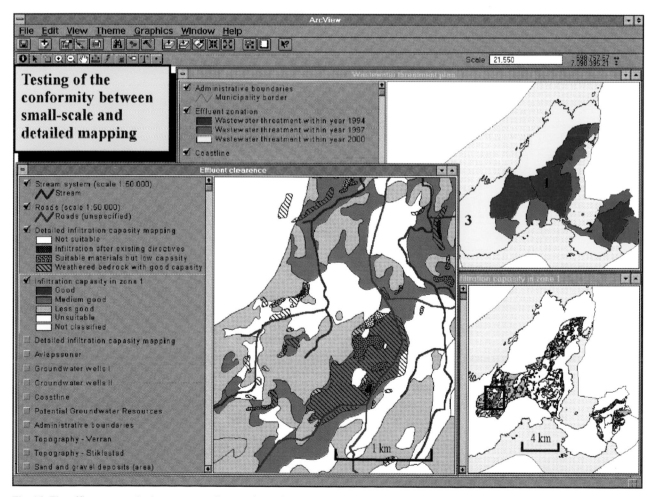

Fig. 15. The effluent zones in the treatment plan are shown in the upper right sub-window. An overlay function has been activated involving effluent zone 1 and the infiltration map (Fig. 13), the result being shown in the lower right sub-window. The proportion of the area in zone 1 that has possibilities for infiltration has been calculated, giving 41%. On the left, a comparison is made between the detailed mapping shown in figure 14 and what we may call the general map, derived from the surficial deposit map.

Mapping of hazardous waste deposits and areas with contaminated land has been carried out in Norway (Banks 1990). The precise location of the localities registered, the type of locality (1: waste disposal, 2: contaminated land) and four ranked groups (1: the need for urgent investigations or counter measures, 2: the need for more detailed investigations, 3: the need for investigations in the event of changed land-use, and 4: investigations not required) can be inspected through the GIS tool. Only one such locality (the Røra dry waste disposal) was registered in Inderøy (Fig. 16). The waste disposal is situated on marine sediments, and possible seepage water will reach the stream nearby. The attribute data in the table in this figure, however, shows in this case that no more detailed investigation are required. Banks (1990) describes this study in more detail.

By combining the digital infiltration map, the local authority plans for effluent treatment, digital registrations of waste disposals, the local authority sewage network, digital property maps and a database on real estate, addresses and buildings in Norway (the GAB database), a comprehensive basis for taking decisions will be available, which should help to ensure that correct solutions are chosen.

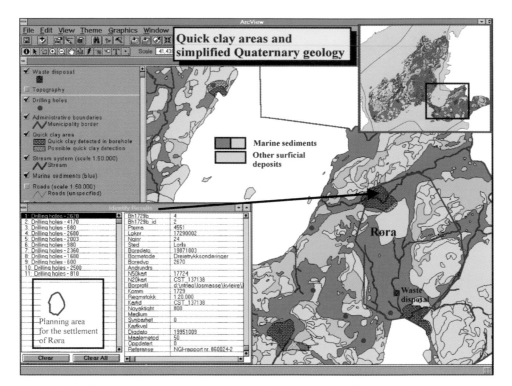

Fig. 16. The surficial deposit map on the right is simplified by grouping all the types of surficial deposits that do not represent marine and fjord deposits under a single colour group (green). Areas representing a certain degree of risk for landslides and the NGI boreholes are overlain. The Røra dry waste disposal site, extracted from the waste disposal site database, is marked, and proves to be situated on marine sediments with poor clearance capabilities. The attribute table from one of the boreholes (at Loraas) is also shown (in Norwegian). The theme showing the stream system is also activated. The boundaries of the municipal sector plan for Røra are also included to enable information in this figure to be linked to information in figure 17.

## 5.4  Landslide awareness

NGU and the Norwegian Geotechnical Institute (NGI) have collaborated to map all the areas in Norway where there is a potential risk of quick clay landslides occurring. The basis was the NGU Quaternary map series on the scales of 1:50,000 and 1:20,000. NGI undertook a delimitation of areas based on studies of the geological and topographical conditions, as well as assessing the results of simple ground investigations by drilling a series of boreholes. Each of these areas shows the assumed maximum area in which a major quick clay slide may occur, but does not include evaluations of the degree of damage a slide might cause or its terminal distance. The results have so far been presented in analogue reports and maps.

The importance of having this type of information available in digital form in connection with planning is substantial. NGU has therefore taken the initiative in respect to the Department of the Environment, the National Fund for Natural Disaster Assistance and NGI by assembling the very first digital map database carrying such information. This is a natural step considering the responsibility placed on NGU as the thematic centre for geological data on the environment. It was decided that Nord-Trøndelag would serve as a testing area for this task since data on surficial deposits for this area already exist in digital form.

Figures 16 and 17 show examples of the production of digital data on landslide risk. Several areas carrying a potential risk of landslides were delimited in Inderøy (NGI 1993). Quick clay was located at various levels within the drilling depths which

reached down to 40 metres. Stability calculations undertaken by NGI show that the stability level may be low in such areas, but is acceptable considering the present land use. Five such areas are shown on the part of Inderøy depicted in figure 16. The quick clay that is a potential risk as regards sliding is almost always overlain by more stable masses, and the simplified separation of themes depicted in the figure shows that these masses need not always be marine or fjord sediments (clay and silt). It is therefore impossible to predict where the most risky areas are situated. As an example, we will look more closely at the vicinity of the settlement of Røra (Fig. 17), where two areas have been registered as potentially at risk for landslides, one beside the fjord (at Koa) and the other somewhat higher up at Lorås. Both the boreholes marked in these areas reached a depth of 26 metres. The GIS tool offers the opportunity of displaying the borehole data log on the screen by clicking the drilling point with the cursor, thus establishing what the system refers to as a Hot Link.

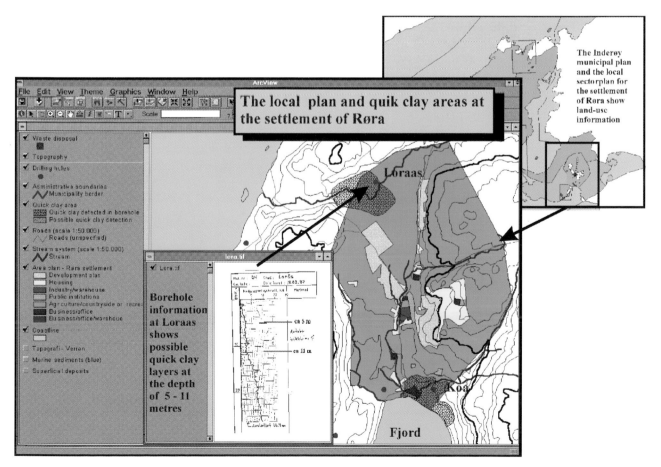

Fig. 17. The municipal sector plan for Røra shows the extent to which existing development is in contact with registered areas of quick clay. The boreholes are shown as red dots. When the cursor is pointed at a borehole and the mouse button is clicked, a hot link function activates an illustration file which shows the borehole profile data.

When the quick clay data are combined digitally with the municipal sector plan, stream systems and roads in the same area, and when detailed information about the depth at which the quick clay is situated is readily available, the chances of reducing the risk of landslides are further enhanced. When areas concerned are crossed by streams and are affected by the road network and building development, new encroachments may alter the stability and cause landslides. The waste disposal referred to previously (Fig. 16) is also close to one of them. Interactive utilisation of such information during the planning process is therefore decisive for being able to increase the landslide awareness.

## 5.5    Other environmental geology factors

The information on the natural environment is an important precondition for being able to assess the effect of any environmental impacts brought about by man. At NGU, the environmental geological themes are chiefly based on analyses and measurements of the geochemical and geophysical attributes of rocks, surficial deposits and water. In this context, information has been acquired in Nord-Trøndelag regarding natural radioactivity, the sensitivity against acidification (derived from data on the bedrock), analyses of proportions of heavy metals in stream sediments, and the quality of surface water. The results reveal large regional differences within the county regarding these natural environmental factors that are determined by the geology.

If we consider the conditions for Inderøy, the natural radioactive radiation from the bedrock (which, with high concentrations, may give predictions of high concentration of radon gas) does not exceed normal levels. This theme is therefore not illustrated in a separate figure. The same applies to the natural content of heavy metals in stream sediments, a dataset that often indicates similar conditions in bedrock, till and vegetation.

Rocks which contain easily weathered minerals, such as chlorite, biotite and calcite, have an appreciable ability to dissolve chemically and to liberate ions into the aquatic environment, thus neutralising acidic water, i.e. they help to withstand acidification. Even if the classification of the solubility of the bedrocks are carried out on small scale bedrock maps (Fig. 18), there is good agreement between this classification and the pH actually measured in streams and small rivers in the same area. The results of a regional overview of the water quality in rivers and lakes show this (Ryghaug et al. 1994). It is claimed that Central Norway has so far been little affected by far-transported pollution and acid precipitation compared with areas in South Norway. The water quality measurements, however, show that the environment in many places is already very acidic from the outset.

The enlarged sub-window showing part of Inderøy (Fig. 18) shows that the rocks and surficial deposits which are readily soluble give high sensitivity against acidification and contribute to high pH values in the river systems. This is obviously a factor contributing towards the position of Inderøy as an important farming area.

The investigation of the content of inorganic chemical components, such as $NO_3^-$, $SO_4^{2-}$, Ca and Mg, in the surface water shows very high concentrations. Particularly notable are the high levels of $NO_3^-$ near Børgin (Fig. 19), which can best be explained in terms of severe pollution and soil erosion as a consequence of farming practices in the area. In the long term, this can have great consequences for the environment of this enclosed fjord arm if the necessary measures are not undertaken. Data of this nature can help to monitor the environment on a regional scale.

## 5.6    Tourist industry

The tourist industry plays an important role as a basis for other activities in the community and in other business sectors. Large parts of Nord-Trøndelag have a marked wilderness character, a feature which tourists from densely populated countries further south in Europe would rate highly. For the tourist industry it is therefore vital that such areas of open countryside are managed correctly so that important sectors of the natural environment or geological objects that are worthy of protection are not destroyed. People have a special and inquisitive relationship with bedrock, minerals and the diversity of forms and structures. Geological information can help to increase the opportunities for enjoyment if it is made available through identified localities equipped with information signs placed along roads or on tracks used by walkers. Many Quaternary deposits and features in Norway, that are worthy of protection for posterity, have been registered (Erikstad 1992). The same applies to occurrences of minerals, fossils, karst resources and geological structures, as well as old ore prospects

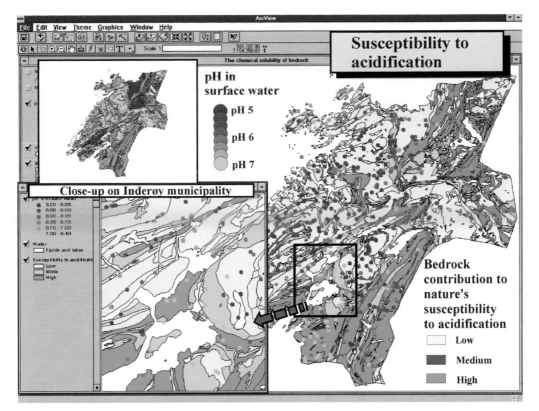

Fig. 18. The solubility of the rocks is derived from the bedrock map uppermost to the left and is combined with a point theme showing pH measurements in surface water. The close correlation between the themes is even more obvious when examined in greater detail, for instance in the Inderøy area in the lower left of the figure.

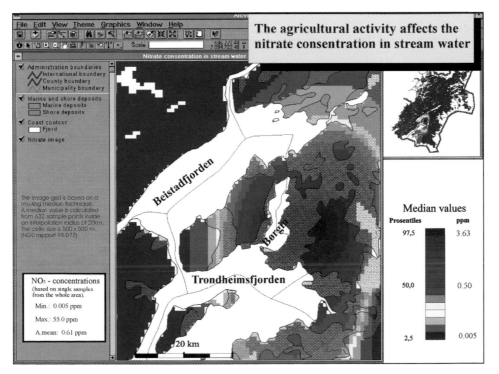

Fig. 19. An overview map showing the moving median concentration of nitrate in surface water in Nord-Trøndelag and part of the Fosen Peninsula (upper right) reveals very high concentrations of nitrate in inner parts of Trondheimsfjorden (dark red colour). The map is a cell-based raster map of the individual localities from figure 18, and is described in more detail in Ryghaug et al. (1994). An enlarged segment of the map also shows the distribution of marine and fjord sediments, which generally coincide with the important farming areas. Pollution from farming is the most likely cause of the high nitrate concentration.

and mines. To regulate their use is often better than to try to keep them concealed from the public. Earth science conservation localities of this kind can be very valuable in an educational context.

Other cultural relics are better known within the tourist industry. A number of these relics and examples of cultural landscape are closely linked to geological factors; for example, rock carvings and their association with a shifting marine limit, or grave mounds, burial cairns and patterns of early settlement viewed in relation to aspects of the Quaternary geology. Combining these attractions with geological information will further their appreciation.

It is important that objects of this nature are recorded early enough, and that consideration is given to them in the planning process. This may be of great significance no matter whether it concerns a feature of national importance that is worthy of protection, an important excursion locality, a nature trail for local educational purposes, or something that can influence the routing of a track for walkers.

A number of Quaternary features that are deemed worthy of protection have been digitally registered in Nord-Trøndelag, and a few have actually been protected. More are in danger of losing their value as an attraction or a type locality, often because of sand and gravel pits and road construction. The way has been paved for better information about these localities, thus enabling an evaluation to be made of what should be protected for posterity. No such earth science conservation areas have, however, been registered in Inderøy.

# 6 MUNICIPAL LAND USE PLANNING

County planning, as laid down by the Planning and Building Act, is intended to co-ordinate the planning carried out by national and county authorities and, to a large extent, local authorities. The county plan may be looked upon as a strategic plan to acquire a co-ordinated set of alternatives for national, county authority and local authority undertakings. It is therefore important to achieve a better understanding of the need for regional geological information at this level. This is now taking place in Nord-Trøndelag through the transfer of a regional dataset from analogue to digital form.

With so many different user interests attached to land areas, and the need for continuous updating of land-use information, a digital form for this information will be a precondition for being able to carry out management in a justifiable manner in the future. At county authority level in Nord-Trøndelag, a major step forward has been taken towards achieving this (Fig. 20). The digitised base map is available containing local authority datasets on a scale of 1:50,000 and county coverage on a scale of 1:250,000. This constitutes the basis for a vast amount of digital information which can now be compiled in connection with planning activities. Every municipal plan and municipal sector plan within the county is now available in digital form, and reindeer husbandry interests are similarly covered. Work is also underway to achieve similar digitisation of regional overviews of cultural relics, earth science conservation areas, open-air recreation areas, datasets defining boundaries of shelter woodland (windbreaks). NGU's goal in this work has been to contribute towards making geological information available on equal terms when

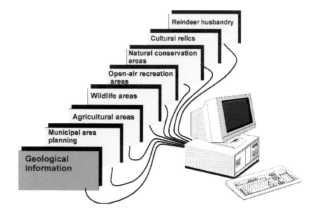

Fig. 20. In the project "Assembly and maintenance of a joint digital database for use in all forms of land-use management and planning in Nord-Trøndelag", the county council aims to make these themes available in digital form to improve the efficiency and quality of all planning in the local authorities and at county level. NGU is responsible for providing the geological information.

future planning is being undertaken with the help of GIS.

Because of the frequent changes taking place in our society today, information will in the future have to be based on more temporary documentation and presentation founded on digital solutions. Planning will be dominated by interactive digital comparisons and analyses (Grimshaw 1994). Particularly in work connected with the development of built-up areas, a great deal needs to be done to combat the regrettable trends often seen as regards inappropriate land use.

The area section of a municipal plan is supposed to show how the local authority will manage its natural resources, such as mineral deposits and groundwater. In municipal plans, the area is divided according to land use. Agricultural, open countryside and open-air recreation areas are divided according to regulations which state how much development can be permitted when it is not associated with business enterprises bound to a specific location. The plan is also supposed to provide information about areas for extraction of material deposits and for building development, as well as those earmarked for specific purposes (catchment areas around water supply sources, areas that should be protected under the terms of the Nature Conservation Act or the Cultural Heritage Act, or regulated as protected areas). This proves to be difficult without a greater input of digital geological information, as can be illustrated by looking at the area section of the municipal plan for Inderøy (Fig. 21) and examining in detail the sector plan for Straumen (enlarged map). There has been a quarry at Hylla for many years, largely producing lime for farming purposes. A bedrock resource such as this limestone will already be affected by a number of forms of land use, several of which will exclude future exploitation. The same will be the case with resources linked to surficial deposits (Fig. 22). Because of the differing attributes and utility values linked to such resources, it is often necessary to undertake specific choices as regards resource use and land use. We must, on the basis of current needs, give priority to which of the surficial deposit properties (an infiltration medium, a sand and gravel resource, a groundwater resource, their importance as good ground for building on or cultivating) we want to consider. Interactive use of the GIS tool permits better classification of areas (assessments which classify according to different land-use values), as well as revealing land-use conflicts to help to ensure that correct political decisions are taken.

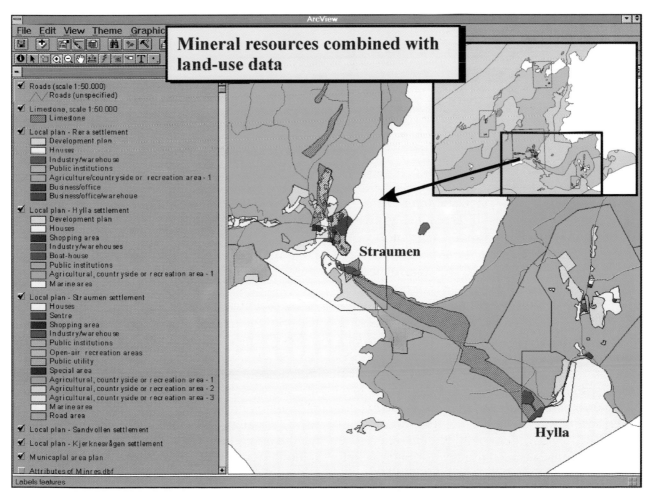

Fig. 21. The municipal plan for Inderøy is shown on the right along with an enlarged segment of the municipal sector plan for the settlement of Straumen. The only mineral resource of major interest in Inderøy (a limestone) is overlain to emphasise the importance of being able to combine different datasets in order to ensure justifiable management of natural resources. The limestone quarry at Hylla is seen in the lower right-hand corner.

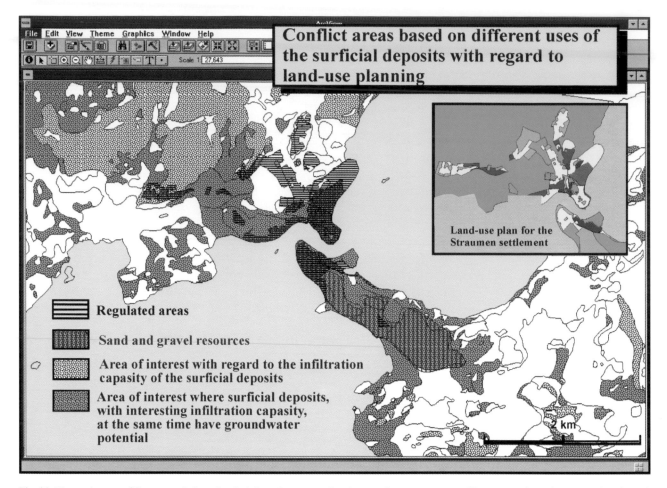

Fig. 22. The settlement of Straumen, Inderøy's administrative centre. Land-use and resource-use conflicts can attain major proportions in such pressure areas. The surficial deposits, with their derived themes, can lead to alternative forms of land use in addition to building ground and farming land.

## 7 CONCLUSIONS

It is easy to observe the transition from an industrial society to an information society. As far as we can see, a need will always exist to print and plot thematic information on paper. In the future, however, the printed map will be only one of several forms of presentation that have their origin in digital information. It is expected that the demands for visualisation of information will increase. Terrain models and multimedia presentations on CD-ROM are already widely used to achieve better understanding of information. The Internet network is predicted to play an important part in distribution of such geographical information in the future.

In the flood of information, all kinds of decision-makers will become increasingly dependent upon reliable analyses and objective cartographic illustrations based on professional assessments. With correct information, including geological information, available in a digital form at the right time, the stage will be set for correct political, technical or economical decision to be made. At the same time,

conditions will be more favourable for a proper follow-up of the results.

Each year the public sector in Norway spends large amounts of money on planning, but far from comparable funds are invested in finding out whether the areas concerned really are used in keeping with the plans, and whether the plans are effective. It must be a goal to acquire stricter control over land-use trends in the local authority sector, thereby improving the control of our natural resources. Greater focus on GIS in local authority management will, in the long term, result in more efficient handling of planning matters, improve co-ordination between parties affected by the planning process and between neighbouring local authorities, raise the quality of impact assessments and contribute towards achieving greater predictability by uncovering conflict situations early in the planning process.

Through improved access to user-adjusted geological information in local planning and administration, NGU wants to contribute to economic growth in the mineral industry, a balanced management of natural resources, improved and cost-effective land-use planning and cost-effective development projects. The examples given in this article have hopefully emphasised this. Digital geological information, in combination with the new information technology, clearly provides an important key to a better decision-making framework.

A continued transfer of analogue geological data to digital form is therefore a high-priority task at NGU and, in common with the rest of the public sector in Norway, we thus have a great deal of work ahead of us. It is our goal that, in time, every county and local authority that decides to use a digital planning system, will be able to carry out their land-use and resource management with the relevant geological information available to them in digital form. When this becomes a reality, we will be able to claim that we have extended our slogan to read "Geology for the whole of society".

## 8 ACKNOWLEDGEMENTS

I would like to thank Janne Grete Wesche, Åse Karin Rønningen and Arne Solli for valuable support in compiling and providing the digital geological data, and to Harald Sveian, Knut Riiber and Bernt Olav Hilmo for the geological quality control besides support on the development work on the derived themes of the surficial deposits. Olle Selinus and Maria Nikkarinen gave constructive comments to the manuscript. Richard Binns translated it into the English language, and David Roberts helped me with some corrections.

## REFERENCES

**Banks, D. 1990.** Kartlegging av spesialavfall i deponier og forurenset grunn i Nord-Trøndelag fylke. NGU Rapport 90.128. 194 p.

**Bernhardsen, T. 1992.** Geographic Information Systems, VIAK IT and Norwegian Mapping Authority. 318 p.

**Burrough, P. A. 1986.** Principles of Geographic Information Systems for Land Resources Assessment. Claedon Press. Oxford. 193 p.

**Christensen, G. E., Grønland, S. E. & Methlie, L. B. 1991.** Informasjonsteknologi: strategi, organisasjon, styring. Bedriftsøkonomenes Forlag, Oslo. 397 p.

**Ellingsen, K. 1992.** Grunnvann i Norge (GiN). Sluttrapport. NGU Skifter 111, 1–35.

**Erikstad, L. 1992.** Earth science conservation in Europe. Proceedings from the Third Meeting of the European Working Group of Earth Science Conservation. NINA Utredning 41, 1–72.

**ESRI, 1992.** Understanding GIS. The Arc/Info Method. Redlands, USA: Environmental systems research institute, Inc. 549 p.

**Grimshaw, D. R. 1994.** Bringing geographical information systems into business. England: Scientific & Technical, Logman Group Limited, England. 288 p.

**Hilmo, B. O. & Sveian, H. 1993.** Løsmassekartlegging for infiltrasjon av avløpsvann fra spredt bebyggelse, Granaelvområdet, Inderøy kommune. NGU Rapport 93.031. 22 p.

**Neeb, P. R. 1995.** Aggregates Resources in Norway. Super quarries an important mining industry of the future. NGU Rapport 95.062. 25 p.

**NGI, 1993.** Faresonekartlegging, kvikkleireskred, kartblad Stiklestad M 1 : 50.000. NGI-rapport 860024-2. 105 p.

**Nikkarinen, M. (ed.) 1996.** Geological Information for environmental and land-use planning. In: Neeb, P. R. (ed) Geological Survey of Finland, Special Paper 22, 9–37 (this volume).

**Nordisk KVANTIF, 1987.** Community benefit of Digital Spatial Information. Report 3. VIAK A/S, Arendal. 219 p.

**Reite. A.** Verran 1622I, Quaternary map, scale 1 : 50.000. Trondheim: Norges geologiske undersøkelse. Unpublished.

**Ryghaug, P. 1992.** Geografiske informasjonssystemer skaper geologi for samfunnet. NGU årsmelding 1992, 10–11.

**Ryghaug, P., Hilmo, B. O., Sæther, O. & Nilsen, R. 1994.** Vannkvalitet i Nord-Trøndelag og Fosen. Målinger av uorganiske kjemiske parametre i overflatevann. NGU Rapport 94.077. 785 p.

**Ryghaug, P. 1995a.** Expanded use of surficial deposit information in local government with geographical information systems. Norges geologiske undersøkelse 427, 104–107.

**Ryghaug, P. 1995b.** Digital earth science information calls for standardisation (data quality parameters and meta-data). ScanGIS'95. The 5th Scandinavian Research Conference on Geographical Information Systems, 12th–14th June 1995, Trondheim, Norway, p. 287–296.

**Sigmond, E. M. O. 1985.** Bedrock map of Norway, scale 1 : 1 million. Trondheim: Norges geologiske undersøkelse. 39 p.

**Solli, A.** Unpublished. Digital bedrock map of Nord-Trøndelag and Fosen, scale 1 : 50.000–1 : 250.000. Trondheim: Norges geologiske undersøkelse.

**Statens kartverk, 1995.** Samordnet opplegg for stedfestet informasjon. SOSI, et standardformat for digitale geodata, Versjon 2.2. 833 p.

**Sveian, H. & Bjerkeli, K. 1984.** Verdalsøra, CST 135136-20, Quaternary map, scale 1:20.000. Norges geologiske undersøkelse.

**Sveian, H. 1985a.** Børgin, CST 137138-20, Quaternary map, scale 1 : 20.000. Trondheim: Norges geologiske undersøkelse.

**Sveian, H. 1985b.** Leksdalsvatnet, CUV 137138-20, Quaternary map, scale 1 : 20.000. Trondheim: Norges geologiske undersøkelse.

**Sveian, H. 1985c.** Stiklestad 1722 IV, Quaternary map, scale 1 : 50.000. Trondheim: Norges geologiske undersøkelse.

**Sveian, H. 1992.** Steinkjerfjorden, CST 139140-20, Quaternary map, scale 1 : 20.000. Trondheim: Norges geologiske undersøkelse.

**Thoresen, M. K. 1991.** Quaternary map of Norway, scale 1:1 million. Trondheim: Norges geologiske undersøkelse. 64 p.

**Wolden, K. & Erichsen, E. 1990.** Compilation of geological data for use in local planning and administration. Engineering Geology 29 (4), 333–338.

65

Geological information for environmental and land-use planning
in the Mid-Norden region
Edited by Peer-Richard Neeb
Geological Survey of Finland, Special Paper 22, 67–104, 1996.

# ENVIRONMENTAL GEOLOGY MAPS FROM THE SWEDISH MID-NORDEN REGION

## Examples from the Mid-Norden area

Edited by
Olle Selinus

**Selinus, Olle (ed.) 1996.** Environmental geology maps from the Swedish Mid-Norden region. Examples from the Mid-Norden area. *Geological Survey of Finland, Special Paper 22*, 67–104, 22 figures, 3 tables.

The Mid-Norden Project started in 1988 aiming at providing basic geological material for use foremost in the environmental and nature resource sectors when prospecting for ores and industrial minerals, in physical planning, agriculture and forestry, as well as in medical geology. Within these sectors, geological knowledge has become of markedly increased importance during recent years. Since environmental aspects have become stronger in recent years, it was decided that the project would also include an environmental geology part. The environmental geology illustrates the importance of using geological data in environmental work and land-use planning and is, in this study, based on existing geological material or material produced within the framework of the Mid-Norden Project.

A number of different environmental geology thematic maps within the Mid-Norden area are presented. They are examples of products that can be prepared according to the needs and requests of users and cover a wide range of environmental geology aspects including protection maps for groundwater, vulnerability to acidification, radon risks, erosion risks, maps showing nutrients and heavy metals etc.

The publication illustrates the importance of geo-science in planning our natural resources and in preserving our environment. It is demonstrated that the Geological Surveys can contribute in environmental geology with the preparation of planning material and the necessary knowledge for processing and interpretation of the basic material. The examples demonstrate that a wide range of different types of geological basic material are needed in order to make the compilations and interpretations necessary for these maps, adapted for decision-makers and environmental managers as well as for those of the general public who are interested in the environment.

Key words (GeoRef Thesaurus, AGI): environmental geology maps, thematic maps, ground water, soils, geochemical maps, heavy metals, land use, planning, Skellefteå, Sollefteå, Sweden

*Olle Selinus (editor), Geological Survey of Sweden*
*Box 670, S-75128 Uppsala,*
*SWEDEN*

*E-mail: olle.selinus@sgu.se*

# CONTENTS

# 1 INTRODUCTION

*Olle Selinus*

Our environment is a combination of both natural conditions (geological, physiological and biological) and the human interferences that affect the living environment and human activities (Bernes 1993, National Atlas of Sweden 1994). An important part of the environment is the geology. The geological environment is influenced both by natural changes (e.g., flooding, earthquakes, volcanic eruptions, etc.) and human impact.

The term environmental geology concerns the interaction between human activity and the geological environment, i.e., bedrock, Quaternary deposits and groundwater. Environmental geology is based on geological knowledge of the resources of nature and risks. It is one of the foundation stones in good administration of the environment and resources.

Geological information is needed in society if we are to understand the effects of environmentally disturbing activities involving overburden and water. Damage to the environment can frequently be avoided if geological knowledge is utilised. If the environmental damage has already occurred, then geological knowledge may form the basis of effective counter-measures or contribute to restricting the environmental damage (Bernknopf et al. 1993, Lundgren 1986, McCall & Marker 1989, Wolff 1987, Montgomery 1989, Lumsden 1992).

In Sweden, environmental work is in the process of transition from repairing damage to preventative activities. Thus, in the environmental sector, geological knowledge will play an increasingly important role.

The Geological Survey of Sweden (SGU) is the Swedish authority in possession of the geological data and basic knowledge that is essential in contributing to the solution of certain environmental problems. Bedrock and Quaternary deposits vary in their chemical composition and structure. Together with other geological factors, this has a major influence on the occurrence of heavy metals, the risk for radon gas, the sensitivity to acidification, water quality, etc. (National Atlas of Sweden, 1994).

This publication is a contribution to the Mid-Norden Project and shows examples of different types of environmental geological maps that are based mainly on existing geological material and shows how geological information can be utilised in planning and environmental contexts.

# 2 ENVIRONMENTAL GEOLOGY THEMATIC MAPS

*Olle Selinus*

Information describing the physical environment is essential if we are to be able to identify solutions to environmental and planning problems. Geological maps provide valuable information in this respect. If we are to be able to conduct successful environmental conservation, detailed knowledge of rock, Quaternary deposits and groundwater is of fundamental importance (Wolff et al. 1990). This knowledge provides us with opportunities for early detection, and thus chances to prevent or repair the frequently insidious environmental changes and disorders in the ecological balance that take place as a result of human activities. This applies on both global and local scales.

Control and monitoring of environmental changes is not possible without detailed knowledge of the entire natural background, of which bedrock and Quaternary deposits are important parts. During the passage of groundwater through Quaternary deposits and rocks, different elements become dissolved as a result of chemical reaction. These elements are transported further and dispersed through the circulation of water in nature. Chemical substances that have been formed or added as a result of human activities also enter the water. Soil water transports pollution down to the groundwater.

Today, the groundwater receives many substances capable of causing severe problems to life on Earth. Perhaps the most serious problems are caused by acidifying substances originating from combustion of coal and oil. The Nordic countries are particularly susceptible since most of the bedrock and Quaternary deposits are deficient in carbonates and other buffering substances. As a result, there is an increased release of metals from soil and rock, e.g., aluminium and different heavy metals (Aastrup et al. 1995). These enter the circulation of water and also reach, via the groundwater, rivers and lakes. This may reduce the possibilities to use groundwater as drinking water. The increased leaching in the soil and release of different metals threatens the productive ability of forests and arable land.

Environmental geology maps can be of help in solving these problems and can be used in projecting work and environmental planning. They can, in general, be divided into different types of maps:

* Resource maps that show different natural resources, industrial minerals and rocks, rocks that are suitable for crushing, Quaternary deposits for building material and road material, groundwater, etc.
   (Figs. 5, 6, 18, 22)

* Exploitation maps that illustrate where building can take place, where cables and pipelines can be laid, etc., in the most favourable manner. These maps also include construction geology maps.
   (Figs. 2, 3, 7, 9A, 9B)

* Risk maps that supplement the former category. These maps show areas with increased contents of heavy metals, areas where there is a risk of radon gas, with infiltration risks, acidification risks, etc. Several examples are given in this publication.
   (Fig. 2, 4, 7, 8, 9, 19, 20, 21)

* When combining different types of information, conflict maps can be prepared that illustrate areas where there is clear risk for conflicts between different public interests, e.g., utilisation and preservation interests related to a natural resource. Thus, these maps can form a basis for decisions on utilisation of natural resources when facing conflicts with other public interests. A couple of examples are included in this publication.
   (Fig. 2, 5, 6)

Examples of areas in which geological competence may assist in solving problems are listed in table 1.

Table 1. Areas in which geological competence may assist in solving problems

| | |
|---|---|
| **Groundwater supply** | Type and quality of groundwater and surface water. Quantity, flow patterns, pollution sensitivity. Intrusion of salt water; acidification; changes to the groundwater level. |
| **Fisheries** | Surface water, composition, pollution sensitivity. |
| **Housing, industry** | Groundwater problems, pollution, infrastructure chemical influence on building material, radon in soil and groundwater. |
| **Recreation, tourism** | Effects of influences, e.g., erosion. |
| **Physical planning** | Landslides. |
| **Preservation, protection of buildings** | Changes to groundwater levels, ground instability |
| **Secondary processing of land, land use** | Physical and chemical conditions, groundwater, material for land fill and landscape planning, areas for waste from buildings and households. |
| **Agriculture and forestry** | Polluted soils; erosion resulting from over-grazing, deforestation; nutrients, pH, buffer capacity, acidification. |
| **Mining** | Soil and water contamination; contamination in the proximity of smelters; groundwater problems. |
| **Waste handling** | Radioactive waste; waste from households and industries. |

Users of environmental geological data are municipalities, county administrations, county councils, ministries, industry, consultants, departments of medicine and veterinary medicine, municipal sectors, government authorities, etc.

In SGU's Directives, it is stated that "within its field of activities, SGU is particularly responsible for providing data concerning application of legislation relating to projecting and building and legislation on economizing with natural resources, etc.". This is a clear directive for SGU to contribute with data and assistance related to, e.g., municipal planning in environmental management, etc.

## 3  EXAMPLES OF THEMATIC MAPS

A number of different environmental geology thematic maps within the Mid-Norden area are described below (Fig. 1). They are examples of products that can be prepared according to the needs and requests of users. Since data are digitally stored, it is easy to introduce new aspects into the maps, to change scales and areas, etc.

Since everything is stored digitally, maps can be presented of any desired combination of data, and new data can be included when required. For example, enlargements of particularly interesting areas of a municipality can be made — the area around an important water resource, a waste deposit, or an industry representing an environmental hazard, etc.

It is also possible to obtain maps for comparisons between different points in time.

For certain parts of Sweden, there are already today relatively detailed geological data, but in other parts the knowledge is more scanty. Nonetheless, it is possible to survey the present status of knowledge in, for example, a map of a municipality. This can be used as a starting-point for municipal planning and then gradually improved bit by bit.

Most maps in this publication have been prepared by the GIS Program Arc/ Info. They will be inlcuded on the CD-rom diskette reporting the Mid-Norden Project.

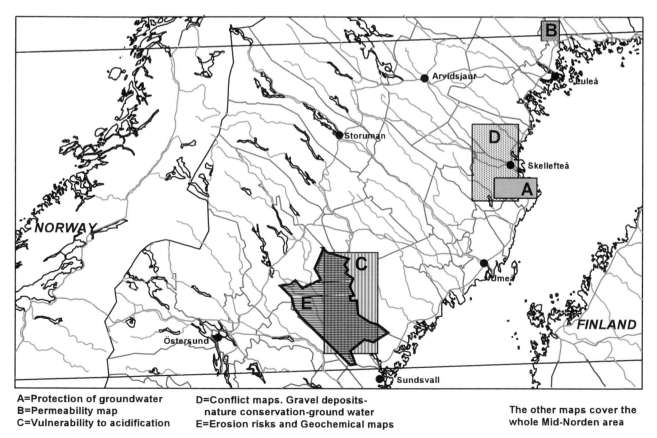

A=Protection of groundwater
B=Permeability map
C=Vulnerability to acidification
D=Conflict maps. Gravel deposits-
  nature conservation-ground water
E=Erosion risks and Geochemical maps

The other maps cover the
whole Mid-Norden area

Fig. 1. Locality map showing the locations in the Mid-Norden area of the environmental geological maps.

73

## 3.1 Primary map for municipal planning of protection of groundwater

### Carl Fredrik Müllern

### 3.1.1 Background

The laws on "Economizing with Natural Resources and on Planning and Building", place requirements on Swedish municipalities to prepare comprehensive plans illustrating how they intend to make use of natural resources in an environmentally adapted and sustainable manner. Against this background it is, thus, of great importance that there is knowledge of groundwater, being a vital natural resource for life, where water resources are located, their size, and also the risks involving unsuitable or careless land use that may in the long run unnecessarily complicate or even prevent the supply of drinking water. In this context, it may concern suitable and unsuitable sites for location of waste deposits, industries handling with environmentally hazardous substances, oil depots, etc. It may also concern the measures that must be taken to protect groundwater in connection, for example, with the building of new roads and, which must not be forgotten, in connection with existing environmentally hazardous installations. (See also Nikkarinen 1996 and Ryghaug 1996, this volume).

### 3.1.2 Basic material for the vulnerability map

The map (Fig. 2) is based on maps of Quaternary deposits in the scale 1:100,000 and on information from archive material from groundwater studies. Using this starting-point, general hydrogeological assessments have then been made concerning the permeability of the different Quaternary deposits and their potential as groundwater storages, as well as of the morphological character, etc., of the different areas. In principle, and on the whole, the map is correct, but as regards more specific, local decisions, more penetrating studies should usually be conducted before a detailed picture can be created.

### 3.1.3 Infiltration conditions

As regards the infiltration rates stated for Quaternary deposits with important groundwater resources, these apply to the vertical transport of water from the soil surface down to the groundwater level. For most oils, the infiltration rate is lower (diesel 0.5–0.2 times that of water, thicker oils 0.01–0.001 times that of water) and for, e.g., petrol it is higher (1.5 times that of water). For transportation further in the direction of the groundwater flow, the rate is directly proportional to the gradient, i.e., the slope of the groundwater surface. As regards oils, even if the oil itself moves very slowly in the soil layers, sufficiently large amounts become dissolved in water to give it a bad taste and will enable it to move at the same rate as water.

In areas with variable infiltration conditions, the infiltration tendency is usually what might be called normal. These areas consist mainly of:

1. Till, where the infiltration rate may vary fairly widely depending on the composition of the till (e.g., the clay content or gravel content). In a sandy-silty till the infiltration rate may be in the magnitude of a few millimetres to a few decimetres per day. If, however, there are gravelly layers, then the infiltration rate may be higher locally.

2. Outcrop. Here the infiltration rate is entirely dependent on the fracturing of the rock. If the rock is without large fractures, then infiltration is very limited, frequently negligible. If the rock is criss-crossed by large fractures, then the infiltration rate may be very high.

   The largest fracture zones in the bedrock usually appear as valleys, generally with a relatively thick, protective overburden.

3. Wetlands: Mires, swamps and bogs are usually outflow areas for the groundwater (the groundwater flow is directed upwards), and thus generally we do not need to worry about any pollution of groundwater in such places; however, there are exceptions. In some areas with bogs, there is a risk of polluting the groundwater but the hydraulic conductivity of the bog peat is usually so low that infiltration and dispersion is extremely slow. In all wetlands, the risk is usually largest where pollution spreads with the surface water.

### 3.1.4 Direction of groundwater flow

The direction of groundwater flow is based on morphological conditions and on the position of the groundwater storage in the terrain. They have only been indicated on the map in areas with large

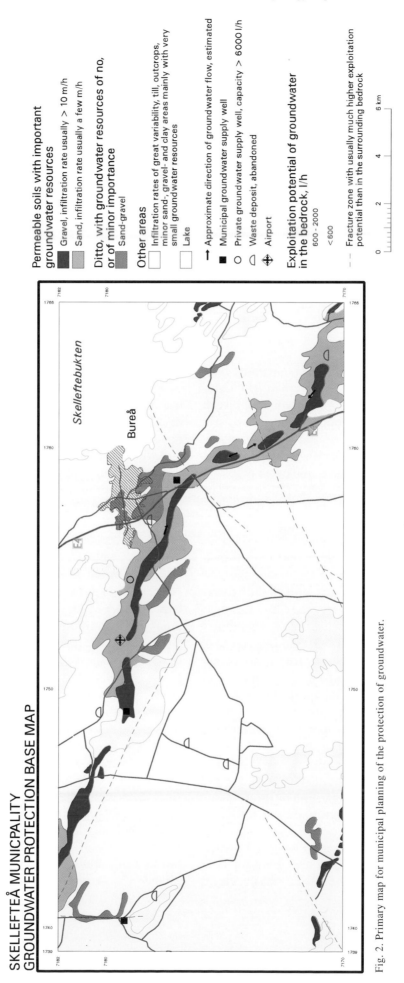

**SKELLEFTEÅ MUNICPALITY
GROUNDWATER PROTECTION BASE MAP**

*Skelleftebukten*

Bureå

**Permeable soils with important groundwater resources**

Gravel, infiltration rate usually > 10 m/h

Sand, infiltration rate usually a few m/h

**Ditto, with groundwater resources of no, or of minor importance**

Sand-gravel

**Other areas**

Infiltration rates of great variability, till, outcrops, minor sand-, gravel- and clay areas mainly with very small groundwater resources

Lake

↑ Approximate direction of groundwater flow, estimated

■ Municipal groundwater supply well

○ Private groundwater supply well, capacity > 6000 l/h

◖ Waste deposit, abandoned

✈ Airport

**Exploitation potential of groundwater in the bedrock, l/h**

600 - 2000

<600

-- Fracture zone with usually much higher exploitation potential than in the surrounding bedrock

0    2    4    6 km

Fig. 2. Primary map for municipal planning of the protection of groundwater.

groundwater supplies.

In an acute situation, we may initially base our considerations on the principal flow direction. However, in some cases it may be essential to have knowledge of the direction of groundwater flow in greater detail. This applies, for example, in the proximity of large wells which may influence the direction of flow to different extents depending on how much water is extracted. However, one must consider that groundwater close to a well will always flow towards the well. Since this may be said to have general applicability, it has not been marked on the maps. Naturally, this implies that, in general, one should stop the pumping of groundwater from all wells close to an emission of hazardous substances and, as a protective measure, construct a sanitation well or take corresponding measures.

### 3.1.5 Vulnerability map

The map is a part of the digitally prepared base map for protection of groundwater in Skellefteå Municipality. It is a map of groundwater vulnerability. It shows an area where several opposing interests are in conflict with regard to land use and water supply.

The map shows infiltration conditions in Quaternary deposits, i.e., where infiltration occurs rapidly, and in other places where infiltration is slower. The map also shows where important groundwater resources are available that may be damaged in the event of infiltration of environmentally hazardous substances. The colouring is intended to function as a simple signal system, where red shows areas with high vulnerability, orange areas with slightly lower vulnerability and yellow where areas have intermediate vulnerability. Areas with high vulnerability are those where the spread of pollution can take place rapidly and where there are large groundwater storages that may become damaged, e.g., in an esker that does not have a superficial sealing layer of clay. Areas with low vulnerability are marked in green. These are areas where the dispersal of pollution to groundwater occurs very slowly or not at all, e.g., in places where the groundwater is protected by superficial, sufficiently thick, clay. (Such areas are not seen on this map.) Areas with a high infiltration rate but without any substantial groundwater resources are marked in brown.

The map shows the direction of groundwater flow, groundwater divides and important wells. It also shows potential environmental risks such as,

for example, large roads with environmentally hazardous transports, an airfield, and sewage plants. It may be suitable to supplement the map with information on petrol stations, oil storages and other environmentally hazardous activities. From this information, it is possible to obtain a picture of which ways hazardous substances may disperse if they are released into the soil. In the present case, this concerns potential pollution sources dispersing towards municipal wells.

### 3.1.6 How to use the map

The map is intended to form a basis when reaching decisions in the overall planning of land use with regard to protection of groundwater resources for municipal water supplies in both the short and the very long term perspectives. When compiled together with information such as traffic conditions on roads — the type and volume of environmentally hazardous transports — and the handling of environmentally hazardous products at industries and similar establishments, it will be possible to use this map also to conduct risk analyses and reach decisions on relevant protective measures.

As can be seen from the map, Route E4 passes through a couple of extremely sensitive areas with regard to pollution. One of these is, in addition, in direct conjunction with a municipal groundwater well. With the intensive traffic on Route E4, with numerous transports of environmentally hazardous goods, e.g. petrol and oil, there is a relatively large risk that an entire community water supply will suddenly be knocked out if one of these transports happens to be involved in an accident in the "red area" at the municipal well.

On the basis of the vulnerability map, catastrophic consequences can be avoided if suitable protective measures are taken in the most sensitive areas. This may concern sealing ditches and road verges, or diverting transports of an environmentally hazardous nature along other routes past the most sensitive areas.

At the airport, which is also in a sensitive area, it may be a suitable measure to construct one or two sanitation wells that can be operated in order to pump up and prevent the spread of any leaking oils and propellants. Alternatively, one should at least establish a specific programme of action for installation of these wells which can rapidly be accomplished if an accident should occur.

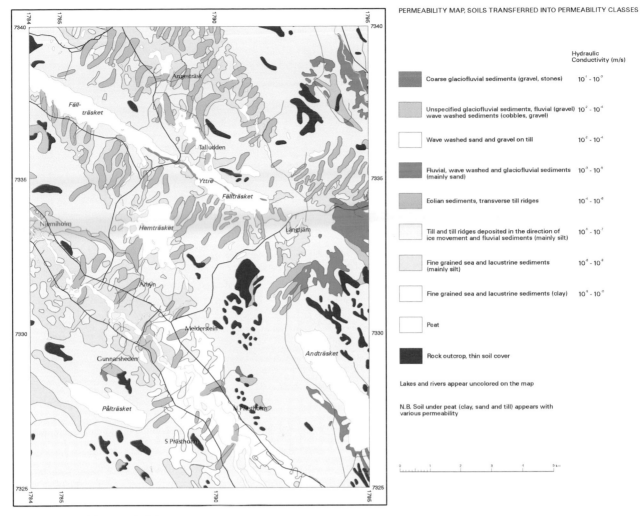

Fig. 3. Permeability map, Luleå area.

## 3.2 Permeability map

*Torbjörn Wikner*

### 3.2.1 Background

Reclassification of Quaternary deposits in an area into, e.g., permeability classes showing the water retention capacity or water transportation properties of the soil may be an important complement to other basic data, particularly with regard to land-use aspects in planning contexts (Fig. 3).

### 3.2.2 Basic material and methods

The area from which the example is taken is located in the northern part of the Mid-Norden area below the highest shoreline. The bedrock consists of crystalline Precambrian basement and the Quaternary deposits are composed of sediments that were

deposited during the deglaciation. Among Quaternary deposits, tills and fine-grained marine and lake sediments dominate. Glaciofluvial deposits are found along large valleys with moraines at right-angles to the direction of the valley, thus indicating the different positions of the ice-sheet during its withdrawal towards the interior from the coast.

The division into classes with different hydraulic conductivity is based on data found in geological literature dealing with the permeability of different Quaternary deposits.

The map has been prepared by, in this case, grouping the Quaternary deposits of the area illustrated into eight groups with regard to their conductivity. Peatland has been omitted from the classification in the present case, together with areas of exposed rock and areas with thin overburden. On the other hand, the underlying strata of the peatland has been classified, which in the present context consists of clay, silt or till.

The map of the Quaternary deposits has been digitised and, subsequently, the Quaternary deposits occurring on this section of the map have been grouped and transferred into hydraulic conductivity classes with selected conductivity ranges.

### 3.2.3  How to use the map

The map has numerous fields of use. In planning/environmental contexts it can be used as a support for helping to solve general land-use problems such as identification of suitable places for groundwater extraction of different magnitudes for both large municipal installations and smaller installations for individual supplies of water. Areas with opportunities for infiltration of surface water in order to achieve artificial groundwater formation can be identified, together with areas where ground infiltration of wastewater is possible. It also offers a good basis for planning of buildings and roads with regard to ground conditions such as carrying capacity and drainage.

As regards infiltration and drainage conditions for precipitation in the area and in different parts in the terrain, the information can be used together with climatological data to indicate the presence of recharge or discharge areas and provides assistance in calculating and assessing the water balance and drainage conditions in the area. Other fields of use might be, e.g. of military interest with regard to the suitability of the terrain for traffic, its carrying capacity and suitability for digging. The map could also be of interest to the forest industry.

## 3.3  Vulnerability to acidification

*Lars Rudmark*

### 3.3.1  Background

Mankind has created several serious environmental problems. Acidification of land and water is a problem of this kind that constantly re-occurs. It is, however, sometimes difficult to establish whether acidification depends on human emissions of different elements or whether it is a result of natural processes (Bertills & Hanneberg 1995, Notter 1993).

Small catchment areas with thin overburden and significant acidic deposition are most vulnerable to acidification. These areas are located especially in the southern parts of the Caledonides and in the coastal zone, less than 50 km from the coast. In the main parts of the inner areas of the forest regions the acidic condition of the surface waters are determined mainly by the soil chemical processes. The role of humus in the forest and bog areas are significant and the influence of the acidic deposition is probably insignificant.

In some areas, acidification has reached the stage where flora and fauna has been affected (Notter, 1993), whereas other areas appear to be completely uninfluenced. Naturally, this depends on the variability of deposition of acidic substances, but this is not the entire explanation. Another and perhaps just as important factor is the soil's ability to tolerate acidic deposits. The vulnerability to acidification varies depending on, e.g., the composition and extent of the bedrock and the Quaternary deposits. Studies have demonstrated that, for example, there is a clear relationship between the geological factors and the chemical composition of groundwater (Aastrup et al. 1995).

### 3.3.2  Basic material

The map (Fig. 4) is based on bedrock maps and Quaternary deposits maps. To some extent, data have also been obtained from other geological studies.

The geological factors that are of main interest are:

* bedrock composition and extent of the exposed rock,

* particle size of Quaternary deposits and their content of rock fragments,

* occurrence and extent of Quaternary deposits,

* carbonate content, degree of acidity and base mineral index of Quaternary deposits.

The geological parameters studied have been analysed by means of a stepwise procedure. In addition, they have been weighted in different ways. Subsequently, they have been aggregated, which has resulted in four classes of tolerance to acidification.

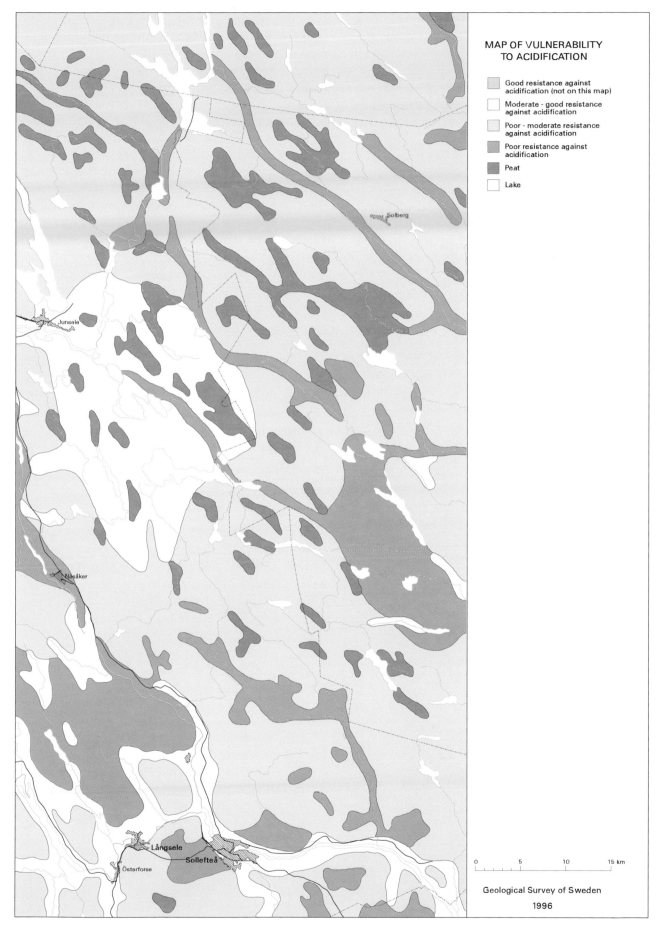

Fig. 4. Vulnerability to acidification.

The definition of this classification is:

1. good

2. moderate-good

3. poor-moderate

4. poor

* In the initial analytical phase, areas where the exposed rock dominates to at least 75% are marked. In such areas, there are no or small possibilities for the overburden to neutralise the acidic precipitation. Depending on the composition of the bedrock, these areas are divided into class 1, 2 and 4. Class 1–2 includes dolerite, hyperite, diorite, gabbro and class 4 includes granite, gneiss, porphyries, quartzite, etc.

* In the next analytical step, the occurrence and extent of the Quaternary deposits are analysed. An area is given a basic classification depending on the dominating Quaternary deposit. In a later stage of the analysis, the basic classification can be modified in either direction depending on the carbonate contents, the degree of acidity and the base mineral index. Fine-grained deposits indicate moderate-good tolerance, whereas sand, gravel and coarse-grained till indicate poor tolerance to acidification. In between these two classes, the classification concerns Quaternary deposits such as sandy-silty till, loamy clay and wave-washed sediment. Peatlands are generally not influenced to any particular extent by the acidic load. These areas are often naturally acidic.

* In the final analytical stage, the carbonate and mineral contents of the soils, as well as the degree of acidity and the base mineral index of the Quaternary deposits are studied and weighted in order to obtain a final class for the areas.

The contents of carbonate, i.e. lime and dolomite, is probably the factor of greatest importance in this context. If lime is not present or in amounts up to about 1%, there is no change in the basic classification. If the lime content is between 1 and 2%, then a change is made with one classification unit, and with two classification units if the lime content is in excess of 2%.

In the studied area, there is fairly detailed information on the till's content of different rock types. In some cases, one single rock type, e.g. granite, mainly characterises a till. In such a case, it will have great importance for the acidification of the area. This situation applies to rocks that are acidic and resistance to erosion as well as to rocks that are basic and easily eroded. Examples of resistant rocks are porphyry and quartzite, whereas dolerite and other basic rocks are relatively easily weathered. If the content of these rocks is in excess of about 10% in a till, it implies a change of one classification unit in the basic classification.

### 3.3.3  How to use the map

The map of vulnerability to acidification is based on geological factors. There are other parameters of importance for the acidification status of an area, for example, height above sea level, soil processes, topography and the composition of vegetation. Despite the fact that these have not being considered, a clear and distinct interaction between the classification given by the geological information and the acidity and alkalinity of the groundwater has been demonstrated. Consequently, the map can be used to make certain estimates of groundwater quality.

A certain relationship between acidic deposition, soil acidification and forest damage and the information in the map can be demonstrated. At present, there is an intensive debate on the usefulness of liming of land and water areas. There are different opinions on the need and benefit of forest-liming (Bertills & Hanneberg 1995). Thus, among many other sources of information for decisions on liming, the map of vulnerability to acidification might be of some help. In areas where natural processes are the major reason for low acidity, the result of liming could be poorer than in areas where the acid load has caused the acidity.

Industrial emissions locally affect acidification of land and water. When establishing certain industries, it should be self-evident to pay consideration to the soil's vulnerability to acidification.

The vulnerability map shows that resistance to acidification in this region is generally poor-moderate or poor. This is because till dominates and that it does not contain any "basic" constituents (e.g. limestones) to any great extent. In the area north of Sollefteå, there are relatively high concentrations of quartzite in the till and this probably reduces the resistance to acidification.

In the area to the south and southeast of Junsele

in the northern part of the map the vulnerability to acidification is generally moderate-good. This largely depends on the acidity of the till. Other areas with moderate-good resistance are found mainly in the south in areas where fine-grained sediments occur in the river valleys.

In the region as a whole there are no areas with good resistance to acidification.

## 3.4 Conflict maps

### Gravel deposits — nature conservation — groundwater

*Karin Grånäs*

### 3.4.1 Background

In order to create a modern society, it is necessary to have access to aggregate material for building roads, making concrete, etc. Almost 100 million tonnes of aggregates are used in Sweden annually. About 60% of the material comes from natural gravel and about 30% from crushed rock. In several regions, natural gravel is difficult to find. Quarrying activities generally lead to conflicts with environmental protection and water supply interests.

In order to obtain good planning of quarrying and good management of natural gravel and other quarry materials, regional surveys have been made within each county. The surveys are financed by a quarrying tariff being imposed on all produced material. In the inventory, the quality, quantity and environmental value of the deposits are estimated. The aggregate inventory is carried out only in areas of low environmental values. The geographical extent, as well as the type of survey that has been conducted (natural gravel or crushed bedrock), has varied from county to county. Information from the surveys is stored in a database, the Gravel Data Archive at the Geological Survey of Sweden.

Every year, reports on the production (e.g., the volume of production, the type of material used, and what it is used for) in pits and quarries are sent to the county administrations. The information is stored in a database at SGU and a yearly report is produced.

### 3.4.2 Basic material

Skellefteå Municipality has been chosen as an example to illustrate the conflicts of interest that may occur in connection with eskers, quarrying activities and groundwater exploitation.

The following is based on material from several sources:

* From the Gravel Data Archive, information has been obtained on positions, volume, composition and environmental value of gravel deposits. The information is obtained from an inventory made in Skellefteå Municipality within the framework of the state survey programme.

* Data on gravel production are those from 1993. The database includes, e.g., the position of pits and quarries given with coordinates and the size of the production expressed in tonnes.

* In connection with the hydrogeological mapping, data have been collected on municipal sources of water supply and large private sources of groundwater supply.

* Lakes, coastlines, large roads and urban areas have been obtained from the digital topographic map of Sweden.

Data from different sources have been compiled using the GIS Program Arc/Info and are presented in two maps.

The first map (Fig. 5) shows gravel deposits in Skellefteå Municipality with environmental value classes illustrated in different colours. All production sites (quarries) are shown and are divided into three size classes. Large groundwater sources and supplies and municipal surface water supplies have also been marked.

The second map (Fig. 6) shows gravel deposits that fulfil the conditions for environmental value classes II or III, and where < 50% of the material composition consists of sand. Gravel quarries and water supplies are shown in the same way as in the first map.

### 3.4.3 Planning of gravel economy

Natural resources must be used in a manner that ensures long-term sustainability. This requires careful planning and decisions on whether gravel de-

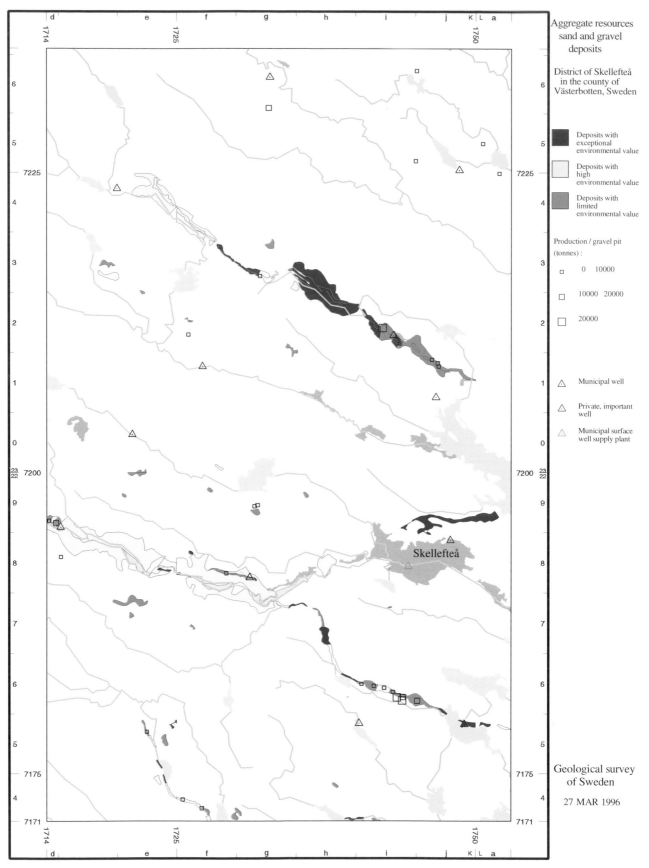

Fig. 5. Conflict map. Gravel deposits — nature conservation — groundwater, map 1.

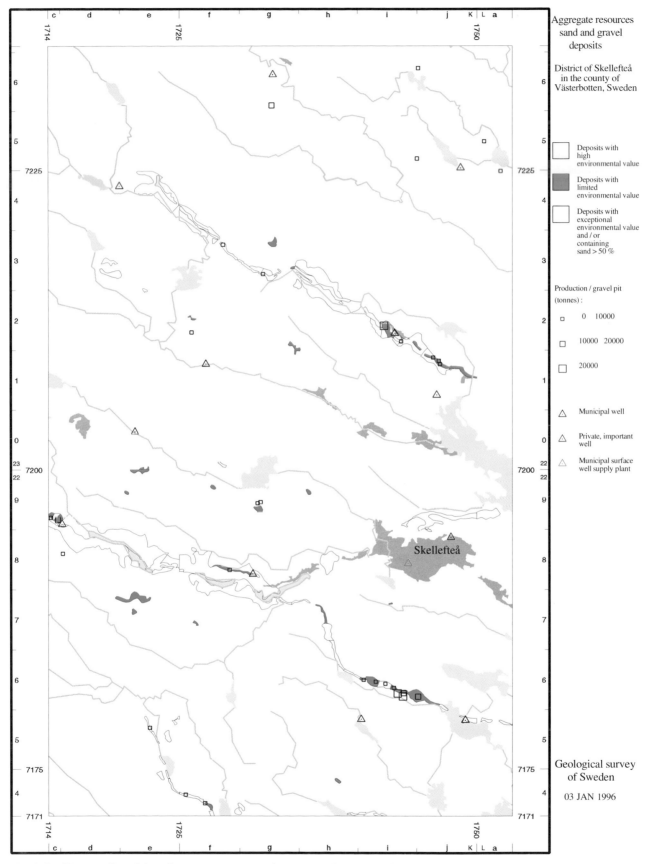

**Aggregate resources sand and gravel deposits**

District of Skellefteå in the county of Västerbotten, Sweden

Deposits with high environmental value

Deposits with limited environmental value

Deposits with exceptional environmental value and / or containing sand > 50 %

Production / gravel pit (tonnes) :

▫ 0  10000

◻ 10000  20000

◻ 20000

△ Municipal well

△ Private, important well

△ Municipal surface well supply plant

Geological survey of Sweden

03 JAN 1996

Fig. 6. Conflict map. Gravel deposits — nature conservation — groundwater, map 2.

posits should, for example, be reserved for future groundwater extraction or whether they can be used for ballast material.

In the gravel inventories, an assessment is made of the total environmental value of the deposits. Deposits with an environmental value class I (red areas on Fig. 5) cannot be released for quarrying. For areas with environmental value classes II or II, quarrying activities may be considered if no other opposing interests are present.

A condition for utilising material in eskers is that it has the correct composition and also, in other respects, that it is of sufficiently good quality. Frequently, the gravel deposits contain excessively large amounts of sand and too little coarse material for crushing. On Fig. 6, only the gravel deposits that have

environmental value classifications of II and III are shown and where less than half of the material consists of sand. This gives a more correct picture of which areas may be of interest for gravel exploitation.

The type of thematic maps presented here of Skellefteå Municipality illustrate that there are few eskers that are available for quarrying either as a result of high environmental values or unsuitable composition. Frequently, interesting areas for gravel exploitation also coincide with important sites for groundwater supply. The maps provide a good base in the municipal planning process where, for example, consideration should be taken as to which areas of land should be reserved for aggregate production and which areas must be saved in order to assure the water supply.

## 3.5 Radon prognosis

*Jonas Lindgren*

### 3.5.1 Background

The radon problem has in recent years attracted considerable attention. In this context, Sweden is a relatively exposed nation since important parts of the Swedish bedrock manifest an elevated uranium content. These include the 500 million year-old alum shales in southern Sweden and along the Caledonian margin and certain granites and pegmatites within the age range 1900–900 million years. Furthermore, the properties of considerable parts of the glacial deposits that cover large parts of the country imply an increased risk for radon entering dwellings. Building traditions, such as the use of light concrete based on uranium-rich alum shale and a reduction in air circulation justified from energy conservation aspects have in many cases aggravated the problem.

In a report published in 1993 by the Institute of Environmental Medicine (Pershagen et al. 1993), the number of radon-related cases of lung cancer was estimated to 400 (200–800). The Swedish Radiation Protection Institute estimates the number of cases to 900, thus qualifying radon to be the major radiation problem with respect to health in Sweden.

More recently, attention has been focused on radon in domestic water as a potential radiation protection problem. Previous risk assessments have focused on radon emanating from the domestic use of water as an additional source of radon in indoor air. Recent studies suggest that the intake of radon-rich water should be considered a risk as such,

especially for critical groups such as infants. The radon content of water has a direct coupling to local geological conditions.

### 3.5.2 Basic material

The following geo-information available at SGU is directly linked with the radon problem:

* Bedrock geology data

* Quaternary geology data

* Airborne radiometric data (uranium concentration)

* Ground radiometric data (uranium concentration, radon concentration in soil gas)

* Petrophysical data (uranium concentration)

* Soil geochemical data (uranium concentration in till)

* Groundwater chemical data (radon in well water)

* Biogeochemical data (uranium concentration in aquatic vegetation)

* GEO- and gamma radiation maps prepared at SGU

A major part of the above data has been collected for purposes other than the study of radon. Correctly compiled, these data nonetheless represent information that can be used to illustrate the risk for ground-related radon problems.

Routines for the use of the above data for radon prognostics are being developed at SGU. In the example below, data on soil, bedrock and airborne radiometry have been compiled to establish the accompanying radon prognosis.

### 3.5.3 Methods

During years of work in the field of radon research, a vast experience has been gathered with respect to radon and its coupling to geological conditions. Routines currently under development at SGU aim at the transfer into computer code of the rules commonly employed by the geologist/geophysicist in charge of the establishment of radon risk maps. The code is being structured as a set of logical operators, operating on the geological, geochemical, geophysical and radiometric information available over the area under consideration. The final product of the process is a digital Radon Prognosis Map showing the expected radon potential of the given area in four discrete levels.

### 3.5.4 Classification

In the regional classification of radon risk, use is generally made of the classes recommended by the Building Research Council, as follows:

* High risk: soil/bedrock containing radium-rich material, such as uranium-rich granites and alum shales (> 50 Bq/kg). Belonging to this class are also soils with an associated high emanation, such as coarse esker material and gravelly-sandy tills.

* Normal risk: areas with a normal content of radium (25–50 Bq/kg), such as gneisses and shales.

* Low risk: areas where the radium content is low (< 30 Bq/kg). Limestone, sandstone, volcanic and basic rocks normally belong to this class, Furthermore, soils with low permeability, such as clays and silts, are also grouped into this class.

The above stated classes correspond to Elevated, Normal and Low radon potentials in the radon prognosis. As the final product is not constrained by any additional ground radiometric measurements, an additional class, Possibly elevated, is introduced. Areas classified as having elevated potential only concern areas where increased uranium/radium concentrations have actually been measured, whereas areas where the characteristics of the ground imply that the area may be radon prone are classified as possibly elevated. The radon prognosis classification does not make use of the simple relations between radon risk and radium content outlined above, but accounts for the specific soil type present and the characteristics of the ground that may affect the radon potential.

### 3.5.5 Radon prognosis Mid-Norden

As an illustration, the Swedish part of the Mid-Norden area has been chosen (Fig. 7). The geological base material used has been taken from the Swedish national atlas. For every soil/bedrock unit, a uranium concentration has been calculated from the airborne radiometric signal over the unit. The soil information has been generalised to a limited number of classes based on the specific radon risk implied for the soil class for a given uranium concentration. The information has thereafter been compiled to a discrete radon potential for each unit. The process means in particular that, to achieve a given radon potential, a higher uranium activity is required for clays than e, g. for tills.

In addition, certain areas with soil types that are known to cause radon problems have been classified as possibly elevated, even if their radiation signature does not indicate any more marked increase. This applies, e. g., to coarse glaciofluvial material.

The map shown should only be considered as an overview of the regional trend of ground-related radon risk as the radon occurrence is known to show large variations in all scales.

### 3.5.6 Conclusions

Radon has in recent years been acknowledged as a public health hazard. The Geological Survey of Sweden is responsible for the mapping of natural radioactivity in Sweden, and disposes information which can be compiled to create products which may help in urban planning with respect to the prevention and detection of radon problems. Recent investments in GIS knowledge and software have provided the tools that enable the rapid analysis and combination of different types of geological information along with the possibility of presenting the results in a client-adapted way including relevant geographic information. In this way, SGU can meet the demands of society for digital radon-related products and also offer expert support to local authorities when dealing with ground radon problems.

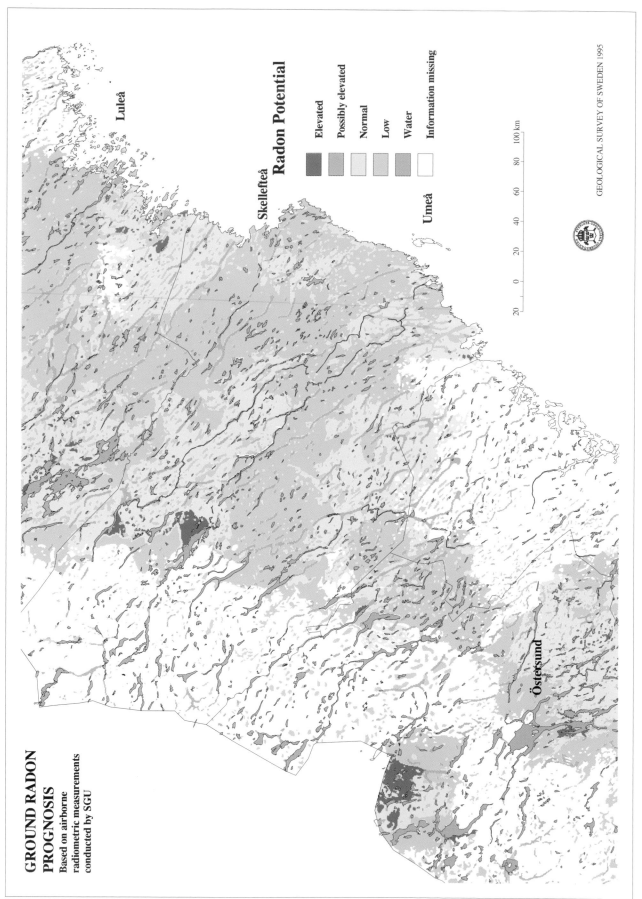

**GROUND RADON PROGNOSIS**
Based on airborne radiometric measurements conducted by SGU

**Radon Potential**

Elevated
Possibly elevated
Normal
Low
Water
Information missing

Luleå

Skellefteå

Umeå

Östersund

GEOLOGICAL SURVEY OF SWEDEN 1995

20  0  20  40  60  80  100 km

Fig. 7.

## 3.6   Erosion risks along rivers in Sollefteå municipality

*Curt Fredén*

### 3.6.1   Background

In several places in Sweden there are areas with high risks for landslides. The bluff and gully areas in the river valleys of northern Sweden are good examples of such places.

Slides and falls are foremost a result of natural erosion processes. However, the development may be speeded up or prevented by human intervention. Slides and falls commonly occur in connection with snowmelt and thaw, and also during periods with intense rain. The common denominator is that both slides and falls may occur without warning.

Falls occur from rock walls and slopes consisting of sand or gravel. The particles move freely.

Slides refer to a mass movement of earth down a slope. Slides occur in silt and clay deposits. Many factors contribute to the instability of slopes. Instability in an area of clay depends on, e.g., configuration of the slope, loading on upper slopes, groundwater fluctuations, clay stratification sequences, pore water pressure in and below the clay, and the clay's shearing strength.

In connection with slides and falls, one usually mentions gullies. Gullies are formed more slowly than slides and falls. They are mainly found in areas where there is abundant coarse clay and silt. Deposits with varying particle size have different maximum water contents and thus different stability conditions. Silt is one type that most easily becomes unstable. If the water availability is unchanged, gully development continues until the erosion base is reached, which is determined by the water surface of the river or the harder bottom underneath. Erosion backwards continues until an area of hard bottom halts the process. A gully is often 10–20 m deep, V-shaped, and has steep sides. Gullies generally branch and have sharp bends. Depending on the topography, a gully may be short or long and have a high or low gradient.

Areas with bluffs and gullies are continuously changing. In place with the land uplift, rivers and streams dig deeper into the overburden. Slopes down the watercourses become higher and steeper. When the height difference — and thus the stresses in the slope — becomes too large there will be a slide or a fall and the slope levels out. The natural processes of erosion thus adjust slopes of different gradients to an equilibrium. Any changes in this equilibrium may release slides or falls. During the past century large slides have become more common, probably because the natural equilibrium has been disturbed by man.

Equilibrium on slopes is influenced by changes in loads on the ground and by changes in the flow of surface water or groundwater. Undercutting of slopes by stream erosion, rapid changes in the level of river water, and changes in the pore water pressure in the slope will also affect stability. Large clear-cuts of forest allow the water to flow away instead of being absorbed, and thereby cause increased erosion on slopes and in valley floors.

### 3.6.2   Basic material, Sollefteå municipality

Sollefteå municipality covers an area of 5,494 km². Its area corresponds to the whole of the province of Södermanland. The River Ångermanälven (Fig. 8), with its tributaries Faxälven and Fjällsjöälven, runs through the municipality. All three rivers have been harnessed for hydroelectric production. The drainage area of the River Ångermanälven is about 31,900 km² and the river has a mean water flow of about 500 m/s. The municipality has about 25,000 inhabitants of whom 9,000 live in the urban area of Sollefteå. Most of the population here live in the river valleys. Within the municipality the total length of the rivers is almost 250 km.

The terrain in the municipality consists of residual hills rising from slightly above sea-level to more than 550 m a.s.l. The level of the highest coastline falls from about 270 m a.s.l. in the southeast to about 230 m in the northwest. The current

Fig. 8. The R. Ångermanälven valley seen from Hallstaberget, Sollefteå. The rocks in the foreground are in the wave-washed zone of the highest coastline. The terraces along the R. Ångermanälven consist of silt and clay, which are partly overlain by sand. Photo: the author, 1995.

Fig. 7. Radon prognosis (on the left).

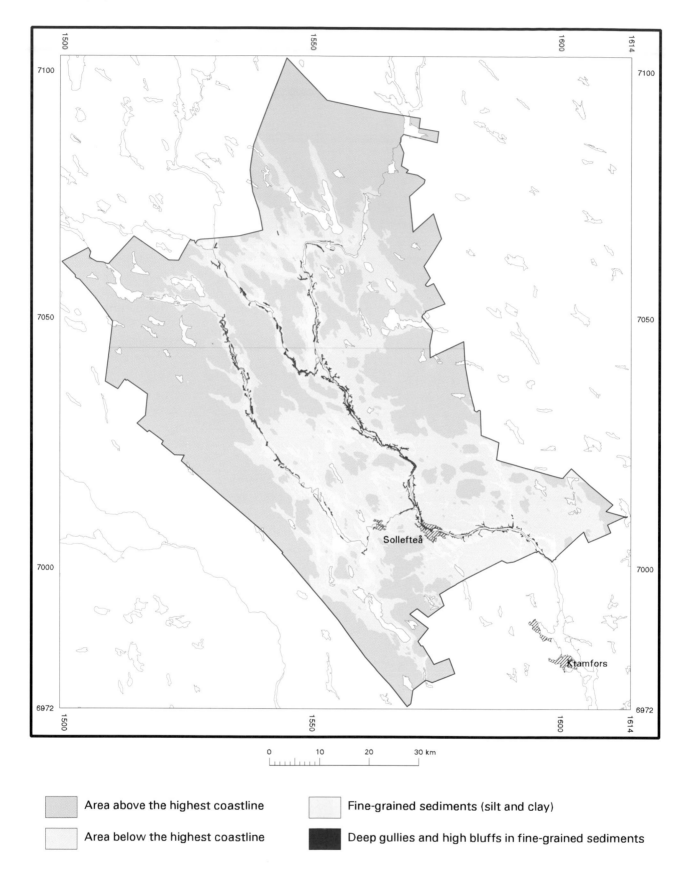

Fig. 9. a) Generalised maps of the area with high slopes in fine-grained sediments in Sollefteå municipality. The maps are based on the Quaternary map of Västernorrland county, scale 1:200,000, sheet 2, and the topographical sheets in scale 1:50,000: 18H NW and NE; 19G; 19H; 19I SW; 20G SW, SE and NE; 20H SW and NW. The isobases for the highest coastline 230 m a.s.l. in the northwest and 270 m a.s.l. in the southeast have been taken from the National Atlas of Sweden.

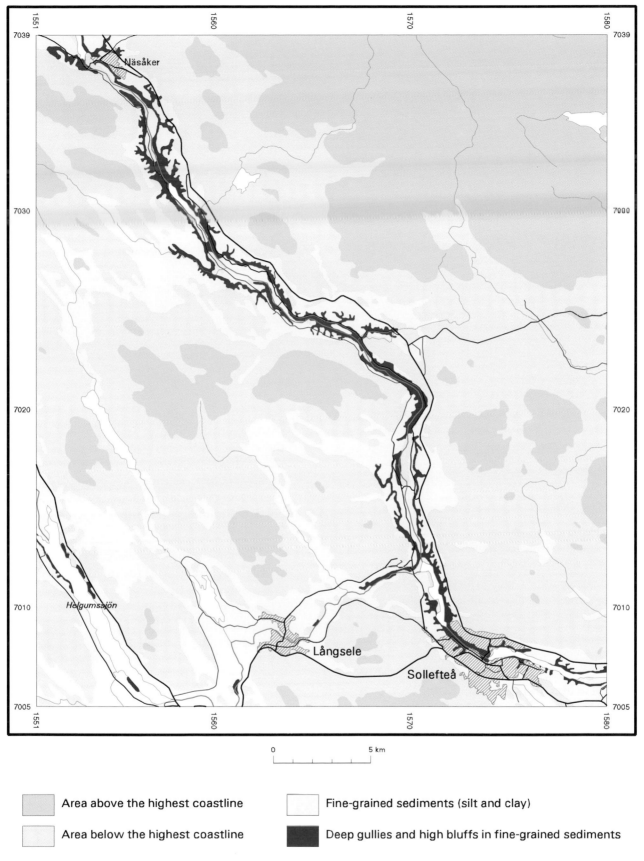

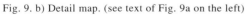

Area above the highest coastline     Fine-grained sediments (silt and clay)

Area below the highest coastline     Deep gullies and high bluffs in fine-grained sediments

Fig. 9. b) Detail map. (see text of Fig. 9a on the left)

rate of land uplift is about 75 cm/100 years. Most of the southeastern part of the municipality has been below sea-level. After the downwasting of the in-land ice, the terrain in this area had the character of a wide, open fjord with numerous islands and skerries (Fig. 9A and 9B).

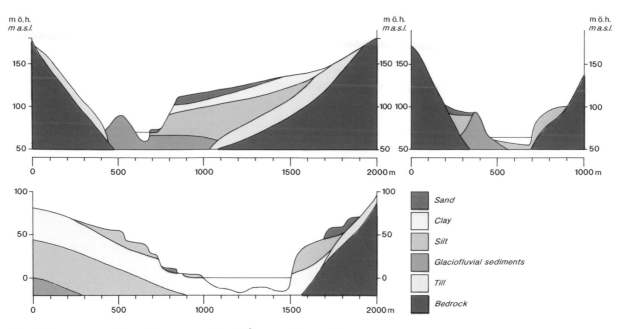

Fig. 10. Transverse sections of three parts of the R. Ångermanälven valley.

The Quaternary deposits in the municipality are dominated by till. In the large valleys, glaciofluvial sediments in the form of eskers and deltas can be found. The fine-grained sediments, clay–silt, are characteristic of the valleys, the central parts of which are overlain partly by sand and gravel (Fig. 10).

Thicknesses of 40–60 m are common in the Ångermanälven valley. Downstream of Näsåker thicknesses of 60–70 m are known. Locally, even greater thicknesses may be found. Thicknesses of about 50 m are known from Faxälven valley and along the River Fjällsjöälven.

The fine-grained sediments can be divided into three groups:

1) Glacial sediments, i,e., sediments connected with the downwasting of the inland ice. The sediment consists of silt, silt with layers of clay, and varved clay. These fine-grained sediments are found in areas below the highest shoreline. Particle size varies depending on depositional conditions, such as water depth and the distance to the ice margin at the time of sedimentation. In the glacial silt the layers of clay are of minor importance, or are missing entirely; in the varved silt the clay layers make up less than half the volume. Clay content is highest where the sedimentation depth has been greatest, whereas the content of silt increases with

decreasing water depth. In lower reaches of the rivers Faxälven and Ångermanälven the glacial clay has a content of 25–50% clay. At levels close to the limit for the highest coastline the clay content decreases in the fine-grained sediments to about 5% and the silt content increases to about 90%.

2) Post-glacial sediments were formed after the downwasting of the inland ice and were deposited in the sea and in lakes. The sediments are made up of reworked glacial sediments and consist of silt and clay of varying composition. They were formed when the river valleys were fjords.

3) The river sediments are the youngest. These sediments consist of sand and silt. They are found closest to the watercourses and overlie the older sediments.

### 3.6.3 Description

The total length of the rivers amounts to almost 250 km within the municipality, which means that there are almost 500 km of river-banks. High banks – higher than about 5 m – are found along a total stretch of more than 300 km and, of these, 232 km are in fine-grained sediments

The areas that are the most exposed to erosion

Fig. 11. Small slope failure in a high bluff. Photo: the author, 1995.

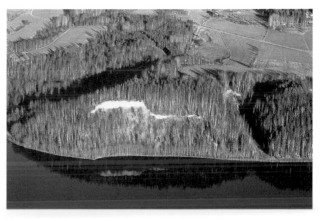

Fig. 12. Initial phase of a slope failure. The snow marks the upper edge of the failure. Photo: Sollefteå Municipality, 1995.

are slopes close to water-courses, Figs. 11 and 12. The height of a slope determines the volume of the slide masses and thus the direct and indirect extent of the damage. Depending on the types of deposits, special attention should be paid also to high slopes in the proximity of the watercourse, Fig. 13, and to gullies, Fig. 14. Most slide scars in the municipality are found along the River Ångermanälven.

### 3.6.3.1 Slides

Most of the scars caused by slides are the result of slope failure. These have not directly affected populated areas. However, the consequences have sometimes been more disastrous than the failure itself.

Table 2. Nature of beaches along the main rivers in Sollefteå municipality

| Watercourse/km | shore | high banks | high banks in fine-grained sediments |
|---|---|---|---|
| R. Ångermanälven | 254 | 165 | 126 |
| R. Faxälven | 143 | 89 | 72 |
| R. Fjällsjöälven | 82 | 52 | 34 |
| Sollefteå municipality | 479 | 306 | 232 |

Fig. 13. Näsåker. The built-up area is on a terrace of sand overlying clay and silt. Small slope failures have occurred and erosion protection measures have been erected on the slope. Note that the slope does not extend all the way done to the river. At high water, the river plain is submerged. Photo: Sollefteå Municipality, 1995.

Fig. 14. Slope failure in the deep Skedom gully, Sollefteå. Note the constructed shore of broken rocks. Photo: the author, 1995.

Fig. 16. A fairly large slope failure occurred during the summer of 1995 in the lower reaches of the R. Ångermanälven. The failure was about 200 m long and about 5 m wide. The bluff is fairly low, about 5 m. The river's water level is almost the same as the the sea-level. Photo: Sollefteå Municipality, 1995.

Fig. 15. Sollefteå. During the evening of 21 May 1967 there was a major slope failure in the high bluff, to the right. The flood-wave swept over the island and washed a cottage into the river. The cottage had been situated in the open area between the two spruce copses. After being washed down the river for about 6 km, two people were rescued from the roof of the cottage. Photo: Sollefteå Municipality, 1995.

* In 1899, Rödsta sawmill, among others, was damaged by the flood-wave from a slope failure in the Remsle bluff.

* In 1967, there was a slope failure in Bruks bluff, Fig. 15.

* In 1859, a dwelling-house was destroyed by a flood-wave caused by a slope failure on the opposite side of the R. Ångermanälven.

* In 1868, a slope failure occurred on the northern side of the river in Sollefteå. On the opposite side a tannery was damaged by the resulting flood-wave. The flood-wave was noticed as far away as 2 km from the failure.

Slope failures may, for some reason, fail to become fully released, whereupon the earth mass usually moves down a few metres vertically. Landslides in low banks generally cause relatively minor damage, Fig. 16.

### 3.6.3.2 Gullies

There are several gulley areas in the municipality. About 25 km$^2$ of this area consists of gullies with varying length and degree of branching. Most of them are found in connection with the River Ångermanälven, Fig. 17.

Fig. 17. In the narrow valley of the R. Ångermanälven the upper part of the gully area is about 250 m from the river and about 50 m higher than the river's water level. The gradient of the gully system is 1:5. Photo: the author, 1994.

### 3.6.4 Conclusions

A survey of the high banks in fine-grained sediments along the three large rivers in Sollefteå municipality shows that there are long reaches that are exposed to erosion. An inventory of scars shows where the risks are greatest and where more detailed studies and measures must be taken to protect life and property. The high bluffs imply that slope failure will involve a large volume of material and, in turn, this will generate a flood-wave that spreads and decreases in strength both upstream and downstream, usually without causing any particular damage. The effect of the flood-wave on the opposite shore may, on the other hand, cause considerable damage and may even initiate new failures.

In a survey of stability conditions, a risk zone shall, thus, comprise not only the area for continuing erosion but also the areas affected by the consequences, mainly the opposite shore.

## 3.7  Soil geochemical maps

*Madelen Andersson & Kaj Lax*

The geochemical mapping activities at SGU have concentrated since 1982 on two different types of media, aquatic vegetation (biogeochemistry) and till. The aquatic vegetation reflects a combination of natural concentrations of elements (among them metals) in soils and anthropogenic pollution. Till that was formed as a result of the inland ice is, on the other hand, generally uninfluenced by anthropogenic emissions. Analyses of this till are therefore important in order to be able to distinguish between the natural and the anthropogenic load on waterways.

Till is Sweden's most common Quaternary deposit and covers more or less the entire country. Since 1982, SGU has been conducting a country-wide sampling and analysis of the fine fraction in till. This fraction consists of particles that are less than 0.06 mm in diameter, i.e., fine sand-silt-clay. During weathering, minor and major elements are released from the surfaces of these particles and thus the fine fraction is particularly important since its total area is so large.

### 3.7.1 Nutrients in overburden

#### 3.7.1.1 Background

One of the most important factors for good growth in agriculture and forestry is the availability of nutrients, i.e., major elements such as calcium, magnesium, potassium, sodium and phosphorus. In nature, one of the most important sources for nutrients is the weathering of rocks and rock fragments in till. The distribution frequently shows large regional variations that reflect differences in the composition of the rocks that have provided the source of the till. By mapping the differences in major element concentrations in till, it is possible to assess the economic conditions for different types of land use. Costs for, e.g., fertilising forest areas can be reduced drastically if we consider the already existing reserves in the ground. This will also reduce the risk of unnecessary over-fertilisation, which might otherwise lead to serious loading on waterways.

#### 3.7.1.2 Basic material

A very common Quaternary deposit in Sweden is the so-called podzol. This consists, when moving vertically downwards, of a horizon containing organic residues (humus), a leached horizon (eluvial horizon), an enriched horizon (illuvial horizon), and an "uninfluenced" horizon that has undergone only minor changes since the time of deposition. Samples are taken in the "uninfluenced" horizon. The depth where this is found varies from place to place in Sweden, generally deeper in the south than in the north since the weathering in the south has been, and still is, more intensive. Normally, samples are taken at a depth of 1 metre beneath the surface.

The samples, taken with a density of 0.15 sample/km$^2$, are freeze-dried, screened and analysed in two different ways. Using X-ray fluorescence (XRF), the total concentration of elements in the fine fraction is obtained, i.e., both the strongly bound (in the mineral's crystal lattice) and in the easily soluble part. If, on the other hand, the sample is leached in Aqua Regia and the solution is analysed with plasma-spectrography (ICP), a more realistic picture is obtained of how much of the element may be released by weathering. There is a rather strong correlation between Aqua Regia leachable calcium, magnesium and potassium and the total amount of exchangeable base cations (TEB). It should, however, be noted that AR also decomposes some clay and other minerals. These do not weather and the potential nutrients absorbed by these are therefore not bioavailable (Räisänen et al. 1992).

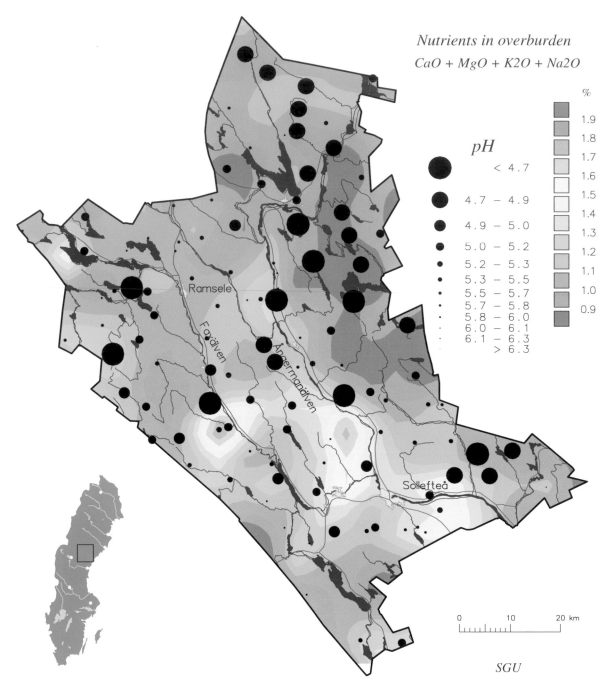

Fig. 18. Nutrients in overburden.

### 3.7.1.3  Soil-bound nutrients in the municipality of Sollefteå

The soil geochemical map (Fig. 18) shows the Aqua Regia soluble concentrations (soluble in Aqua Regia) in the form of oxides for the potential nutrients calcium, magnesium, potassium and sodium in the fine fraction of the till in Sollefteå Municipality. The high concentrations are indicated in yellow to orange, and the low concentrations are shown in blue. Black circles show the pH-value in the till.

The map shows that a zone to the southwest of the line Sollefteå-Ramsele is largely more favourable from the fertility point of view than the northeastern area owing to the higher leachable $CaO+MgO+K_2O+Na_2O$-concentrations. The high concentrations depend on the presence of easily weathered rocks in the till. Typical, favourable rocks are limestones, shales and greenstones. Granites, quartzites and gneiss are examples of slowly weathered rocks. If these rocks dominate the till, then the fertility is drastically reduced at the same time as the susceptibility to acidification increases. Even a minor percentage of easily weathered rocks in the till will markedly increase fertility.

Thus, the map can be used for forestry planning. In areas with high potential nutrient concentrations (light green to orange) we may assume that the natural concentrations are sufficiently high for good growth. On the other hand, growth conditions are probably not as favourable within the blue areas.

### 3.7.1.4 Conclusions

Nutrients in the soil are an important aspect when planning economic and environmentally correct land use. The soil geochemical maps produced at SGU can be used for both public and private establishments in order to facilitate decision-making in different land-use questions.

## 3.7.2 Buffer capacity and pH in till

### 3.7.2.1 Background

The geochemical status of the soil has a strong influence on groundwater quality. During its way through the soil, the rain-water is exposed to a number of chemical processes. Among these processes, there are different buffering systems that depend on the mineral composition of the soil and are of great importance for neutralisation of acidic rain-water. Acidic rain-water in combination with the lack of, or deficient, neutralising capacity, may lead to undesirable consequences for the ecosystems that are dependent on the water (Karltun 1995).

If the soil contains lime, then a carbonate buffering system takes over and acidic water is efficiently neutralised. The pH-values in such areas are high, generally > 6.2. The lack of limestone leads to lower pH-values. At pH-values between about 6.2 and 4.5, neutralisation occurs as a result of the soil minerals allowing the acidic hydrogen ions to "change place" with beneficial base cations, i.e, nutrients such as calcium, magnesium and potassium, whereby there is an increased flow of these ions into the groundwater. This system is much slower and less effective than carbonate buffering.

A critical situation arises when the pH-value in the ground falls below 4.5, which implies that the ground's reserve of exchangeable, beneficial base cations is temporarily depleted. Such situations may easily arise if the content of easily-weathered minerals in the ground is low. In such a situation, a third buffering system is activated, whereby otherwise slowly soluble aluminium compounds are dissolved, i.e., aluminium is mobilised. This process is rapid and effective and thus high concentrations of aluminium may suddenly appear in the groundwater. In addition, the decrease in pH may lead to mobilisation of other hazardous metals (e.g., cadmium). Large parts of Sweden are risk areas since the bedrock is commonly dominated by rocks with low contents of easily weathered material, such as granites, gneisses and sandstones.

### 3.7.2.2 Basic material

Within the framework of the SGU soil geochemical mapping programme, a number of the collected till samples have been analysed with regard to pH and buffering capacity. After freeze-drying, 2 g of the sample is suspended in 10 ml of distilled water and, after about 2 days, the pH value of the solution is measured. Subsequently, hydrogen ions are added in the form of a weak solution of sulphuric acid, whereupon the pH value is again measured after a certain period. Both these measurements constitute the basis for the preparation of maps of the ground's buffering capacity and present pH value. In addition, all samples within the mapping project are tested for lime by addition of strong hydrochloric acid. It should be mentioned that the drying and storage of samples will result in a changing of the pH with time. Therefore, we will not expect to get the same pH in stored samples as in fresh naturally moist samples.

Since only part of the till samples are exposed to the above treatment, no detailed interpretation of the pattern should be made. For the same reason, a detailed comparison cannot be made with the element maps. On the other hand, large common features can be seen, which facilitate identification of weak regions, i.e., regions with low pH, low leachable concentrations of calcium and magnesium, and high concentrations of heavy metals (cadmium, lead, etc.). The till is sampled at a depth where chemical or biological processes have only slightly influenced its original composition since the last glacial period, which makes it suitable for predicting potential risk areas.

*SOLLEFTEÅ MUNICIPALITY*

*Soil Geochemistry*
*Buffer Capacity*

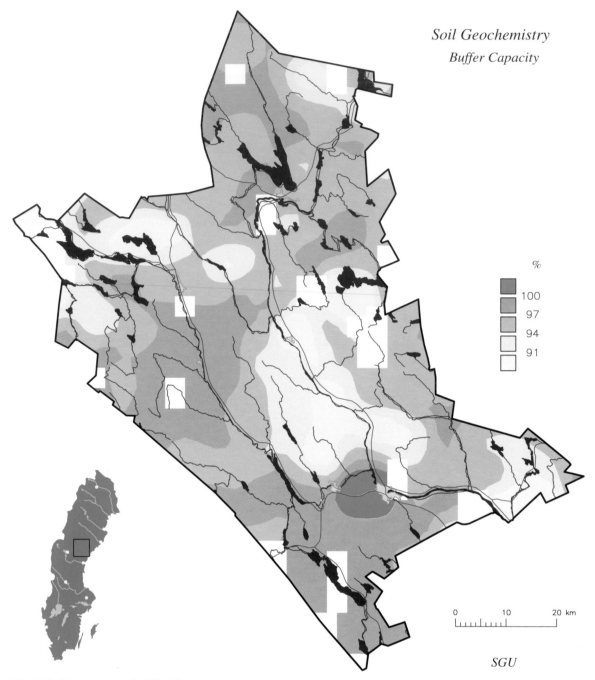

%

100
97
94
91

SGU

Fig. 19.Buffer capacity and pH in till.

### 3.7.2.3 Buffer capacity and pH in the municipality of Sollefteå

The maps (Fig. 18 and 19) show that the ground within Sollefteå Municipality has strong, varying pH values and tolerance to acidification (buffering capacity). Just to the west of Sollefteå, the blue colouring indicates that lime is present in the till. In other respects, the map of pH measurements shows that large areas normally have pH values between 5.8 and 4.7 (Fig 18). The map of buffering capacity (Fig 10) shows, similarly, that large areas may be problematical since there is a risk for aluminium leaching (red and orange).

### 3.7.2.4 Conclusions

Information on the ground's geochemical status

in the form of buffering capacity and pH-value is of great value for land-use planning. This is important not least when considering the potentially extremely negative effects that so-called weak areas may have on human welfare. Several metals in the groundwater that are released when the buffering system is changed may lead to different diseases (Selinus et al. 1996). By making use of information obtained from SGU's soil geochemical mapping, society can obtain a survey of potential risk areas. When planning forest ditching, clear-cuts, etc., that lead to changes in the soil geochemical processes, such information should be considered. In this way, comprehensive measures in weak areas can be avoided and resources for subsequent management can be given priority in areas that are already exposed.

### 3.7.3 Heavy metals in till

#### 3.7.3.1 Background

Contents of metals in our environment depend not only on pollution caused by anthropogenic activities (Notter 1993). Some rocks contain high concentrations of potentially hazardous heavy metals, a fact that is reflected in the Quaternary deposits. If these metals are mobilised as a result of changes to the environment, such as modified land use or acid rain, the consequences for plants and animals may be disastrous. Since pollution may also lead to heavy metal loading on the environment, it is essential to be able to distinguish the natural components from the anthropogenic (See also Nikkarinen 1996, this volume).

Another aspect of metal concentrations in the ground concerns their function as nutrients. Some of the metals in our environment function as nutrients in "suitable" concentrations (e.g., copper and zinc). Excessively high concentrations may thus lead to toxic effects, whereas excessively low concentrations may lead to deficiency-related disorders.

#### 3.7.3.2 Basic material

The ongoing soil geochemical sampling programme at SGU today includes more than 12,000 samples of till taken well outside of urban areas, thus offering good opportunities to investigate the regional, natural variations in concentrations for several metals in the fine fraction of the till. SGU has made a classification based on existing material. Eight metals (arsenic, cobalt, chromium, copper, nickel, lead, vanadium and zinc) have been analysed by X-ray fluorescence (XRF) and divided

into four classes; very low concentrations, low concentrations, moderate concentrations, and high concentrations.

1–2) Classes one and two make up background concentrations and require no measures.

3) Class three also probably is a background concentration but the source should be investigated.

4) Class four, i.e., high concentrations, depends on pollution (natural or anthropogenic) and the source should be investigated.

The border between class three and class four has been placed so that consideration has been taken to a critical factor, i.e., the lowest relative increase in concentration above the actual background concentration that has been found to give a negative effect in forest mor (raw humus) and agricultural soils. Normally, the limit is then at the 95th percentile. Maps based on this classification have been prepared by giving the classes different colours: dark blue (class one), light blue (class two), yellow (class three) and red (class four).

The till that forms the basis for the soil geochemical mapping has been taken from depths where little or no chemical changes have taken place since the formation of the till. It should be observed that the classification is based on total contents in the fine fraction of the samples. Thus, it is possible that some of the metals are so strongly bound within the mineral crystal lattice that they are not mobilised without strong attacks of acidic compounds. Consequently, it may be possible that an analysis of the acid-soluble concentrations in the till may be more suitable from an environmental geological viewpoint but, nonetheless, the total concentrations give an indication of potential risk areas.

#### 3.7.3.3 Arsenic concentrations in the soils in the municipality of Sollefteå

Of the eight heavy metals studied, arsenic has been selected (Fig. 20) as an example since arsenic is an element with documented hazardous effects on the human organism. The annexed map shows that large parts of Sollefteå Municipality have arsenic concentrations in classes three and four. If we consider all samples included in the material, we can see that large parts of southeastern Norrland have similar tendencies, i.e., large areas within

Geological Survey of Finland, Special Paper 22
*Olle Selinus (ed.)*

*Arsenic in Soils*

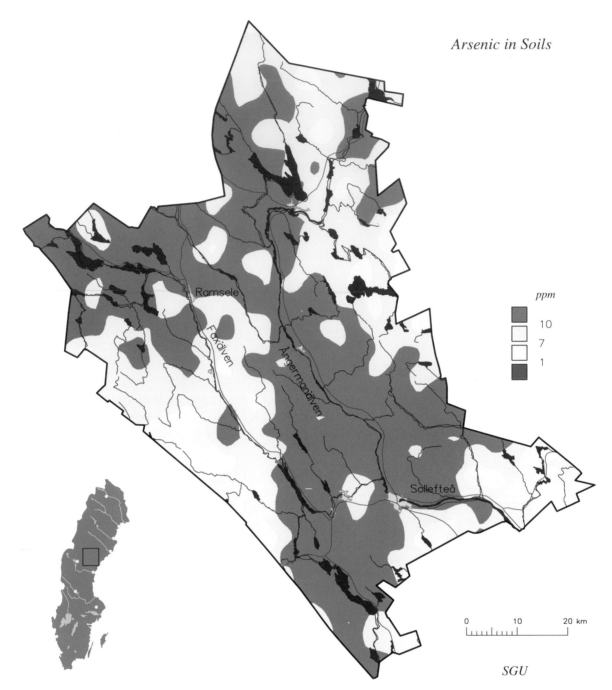

Fig. 20. Arsenic in till.

SGU

classes three and four. The reasons for this have not been fully established, but a common reason for increased arsenic concentrations is the presence of sulphide mineralisations in the bedrock.

### 3.7.3.4 Conclusions

By studying the variations in concentration in the ground, society can localise risk areas where negative effects depending on excessively high or low concentrations in tills may occur. Using information that can be obtained from SGU's ongoing soil geochemical mapping programme, such areas can be localised. In this way, planning of future land use can be facilitated. In addition, subsequent management measures can be introduced in a suitable and economic manner.

Since the geochemical processes cause effects

not only in soil but also in water and ecosystems, other aspects should also be considered. Important aspects are, e.g., soil acidity (pH), buffering capacity, hydrological conditions, and already ongoing metal loading. By means of SGU's mapping of aquatic vegetation, areas that are already loaded can be localised. The soil geochemical maps are useful when trying to distinguish between anthropogenic and natural sources for anomalous areas as displayed by analyses of aquatic vegetation (see below). In addition, the maps identify potential risk areas where the heavy metal load has not yet occurred, but the changes in land use may lead to serious effects.

## 3.8  Heavy metals in drainage systems (Biogeochemistry)

*Olle Selinus*

### 3.8.1  Background

A nation-wide biogeochemical survey has been in progress since 1982 at SGU to map the metal load in the Swedish natural environment and the chemical variation in overburden and natural waters (Brundin et al.1988). This includes the influence of both the composition of the bedrock and the effects resulting from atmospheric deposits and emissions. The survey provides a regional picture of the frequently strongly varying background concentrations of, e.g., heavy metals in the environment which are of decisive importance in discussions on environmental pollution, acidification, etc. This also gives a wide picture of anthropogenic metallic pollution. Anthropogenic activities causing increased concentrations are mainly discharges into water and the atmosphere; and in addition, agricultural activities may also cause heavy metal pollution.

The samples consist of a variety of roots of sedges, meadow sweet, aquatic mosses, etc., from the edges of streams. Together with the bedrock and overburden, they provide best agreement with regard to the distribution of heavy metals. Emissions and deposits are also registered relatively immediately by the samples. The method of chemically investigating roots and mosses is based on the fact that plant roots in a river channel will accumulate ions from the water passing by. The groundwater receives a concentration of metals that largely reflect the chemical composition in the surrounding rocks and Quaternary deposits. When the groundwater reaches a surface water course, there is a precipitation of these metals. Enrichment occurs both in the plant roots themselves and in iron and manganese hydroxides (Selinus, 1983). The exchange of metals between water and the roots is a slow process where influence from seasonal variations is of secondary importance, which implies that the samples reflect an average metal content. The variation between different years is small for most heavy metals.

An important factor for the uptake of metals in aquatic plants is the chemical form of the metals and their mobility. The solubility of many heavy metals increases with increased acidity, e.g., in cadmium, zinc, copper and nickel. On the other hand, arsenic, molybdenum and selenium form slowly dissolved compounds in acidic soils and more easily soluble compounds in alkaline soils. Thus, the acid-base status of the soil is of extremely great importance for the occurrence of metals in stream water and thus also for the uptake in aquatic plants.

The number of sampling points per topographical map is about 100, which gives a density of 0.15 samples/km$^2$. All samples are analysed by X-ray fluorescence for the following elements, among others: aluminium, arsenic, barium, calcium, cobalt, chromium, copper, potassium, magnesium, molybdenum, niobium, sodium, nickel, phosphorus, lead, rubidium, sulphur, silica, strontium, titanium, uranium, vanadium, tungsten, yttrium, zinc and zirconium. Every fifth sample is further analysed by atomic absorption for mercury, selenium and cadmium.

The number of samples taken hitherto (1995) amounts to about 30,000. Mainly southern and central Sweden and parts of Central Norrland have been sampled. However, the sampling is moving successively towards the north. Altogether, there are 4,000 biogeochemical samples available today within the Mid-Norden area.

Since the mapping is done on a nation-wide basis and already today covers an important part of Sweden, this provides a unique opportunity to study the relationship between environmentally related diseases and exposure to heavy metals both locally and regionally. An important factor is also the fact that the geochemical investigations are based on organic material which, in turn, means that information is obtained on metal concentrations that are bioavailable to plants. The material mentioned is digitally stored and can be used for these comparative studies.

# SOLLEFTEÅ MUNICIPALITY

*Biogeochemistry*

*Cadmium (Cd)*

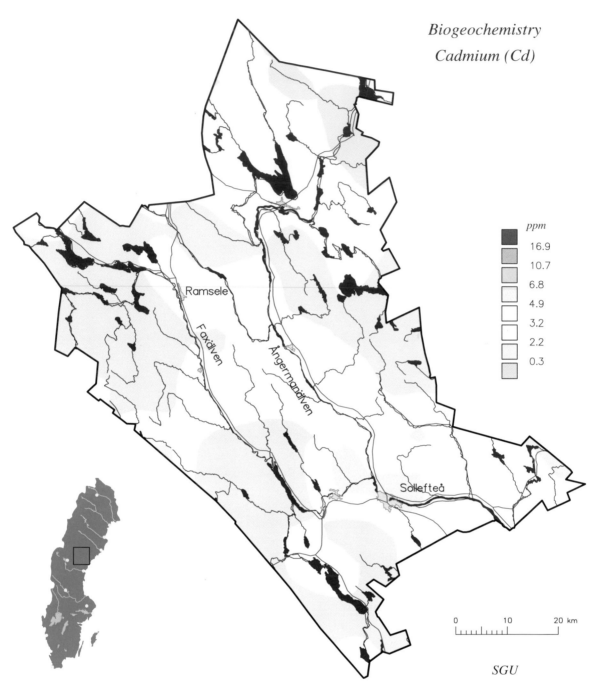

| | ppm |
|---|---|
| | 16.9 |
| | 10.7 |
| | 6.8 |
| | 4.9 |
| | 3.2 |
| | 2.2 |
| | 0.3 |

0     10     20 km

*SGU*

Fig. 21. Cadmium in biogeochemical samples.

### 3.8.2 Biogeochemical map of the municipality of Sollefteå

Cadmium (Fig. 21) is one of the most toxic metals and is essential neither to plants nor to animals. Cadmium contents are low in most rocks but increased concentrations are found in alum shales and sulphide mineralisations. Cadmium follows zinc in the geochemical cycle, but has a higher solubility than this metal. Consequently, in acidified areas, there is a major risk that cadmium will reach the groundwater and become dispersed over large areas. This has occurred along the west coast of Sweden, among other places, where there is massive cadmium deposition in combination with acidic rain and, in addition, where there are rocks and overburden with poor resistance to acidification. In the converse situation, cadmium is fixed in the soil and subsoil in areas with lime-rich rocks with good resistance to acidification, and thus the watercourses are not polluted.

The cadmium contents on the map are low in relation to the contents otherwise in Sweden. Increased contents can, however, be seen along the river, and especially near the town of Sollefteå. In these areas there are no known occurrences of bedrock elevated in cadmium. Therefore, the origin of cadmium in these areas is probably anthropogenic, from industrial activities and the use of fertilizers in farming.

### 3.8.3 How to use the map

The biogeochemical maps show whether a metal is available in large or small amounts to the stream plants. We can therefore see where the highest concentrations are to be found and where there is the greatest need for corrective measures. In conjunction with mineralisation or ore deposits, the natural concentrations of some metals may be so high that they can be compared with the worst form of pollution. Groundwater used as drinking water or for irrigating crops grown within such areas may therefore contain concentrations of metals which constitute a direct health hazard.

Initially, it is not always possible to establish reliability where there are high concentrations of metals within a certain area. The fact that plants contain high concentrations of metals shows, however, that the metals are, nonetheless, present and in bioavailable form.

Knowledge of the amounts of metals present under natural conditions will also allow us to identify the areas where there are either too few essential metals or too many hazardous metals. At present, it is impossible to state that a certain concentration of a metal in plant roots will lead to deficiency or over-exposure to plants, animals or man within the region in question. Nonetheless, knowledge of the variation in concentrations of metals within a region helps us to identify where further studies may be needed on how they have dispersed in the nutrient chains and, thereby, how they may be expected to affect us. In this way, the variation of the cadmium content in stream plants, as one example, has been found to show good agreement with the cadmium content in wheat. In areas where stream plants contain high levels of cadmium, we also find high concentrations of cadmium in wheat caused by e.g. the use of fertilizers. In other areas, where availability of cadmium is lower, the opposite applies. There is also a close correlation with the metal contents in drinking water in wells and in animals, e.g. liver and kidney in moose (Selinus et al.1996). The biogeochemical information can therefore be used as a basis for research in environmentally related diseases (medical geology).

## 3.9  Geological objects of national interest

*Curt Fredén*

Protection of an area is the foremost instrument in nature conservation to preserve valuable natural environments and the geological diversity in the countryside. There are different types of area protection, all of which are supported by legislation in the Law on Nature Conservation:

* National park

* Nature reserve

* Nature conservation area

* Natural monument

Within all these types of area protection, geoscientific objects of national interest may be found. An object of national interest refers to phenomena with few equivalents in the country. Some national objects are also of international interest, mainly reference sites or fossils occurrences. Within the Swedish part of the Mid-Norden area there are two national parks, Björnlandet and Skuleskogen. Nature reserves of large areal extent and with numerous geo-scientific objects occur mainly in the mountain region.

About 23 geo-scientific types of objects are found in the Swedish part of the Mid-Norden area (Fig. 22), apart from geo-scientifically valuable types of landscape such as Höga Kusten (High Coast) in Ångermanland and the Lake Storsjö area in the province of Jämtland. When working on this mapping scale, it has been essential to make combinations and selections. Of the more than 200 geoscientific objects, 3 are located in Skuleskogen's National Park, 97 in nature reserves and 3 in nature conservation areas.

Among objects of national interest for nature conservation, the geo-scientific forms have a prominent position. The distribution of the geo-scientific objects of national interest show regional characteristics for this Mid-Norden area and also for Sweden as a whole. For example, the highest val-

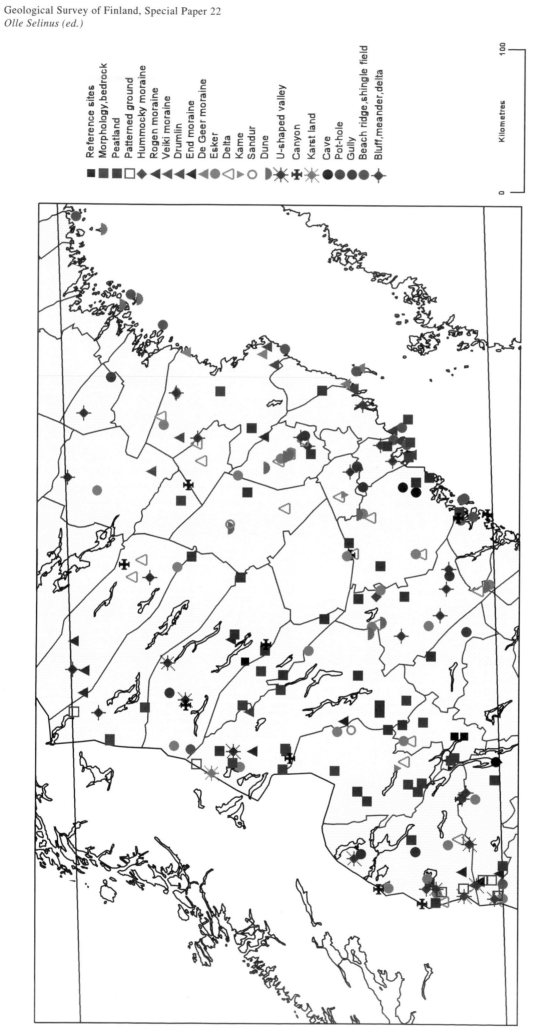

Reference sites
Morphology, bedrock
Peatland
Patterned ground
Hummocky moraine
Rogen moraine
Veiki moraine
Drumlin
End moraine
De Geer moraine
Esker
Delta
Kame
Sandur
Dune
U-shaped valley
Canyon
Karst land
Cave
Pot-hole
Gully
Beach ridge, shingle field
Bluff, meander, delta

Kilometres

0          100

Fig. 22. Geological objects of national interest, Mid-Norden project.

Table 3. List and number of geological objects of national interest listed in the Swedish part of the Mid-Norden area.

| | Number |
|---|---|
| **REFERENCE SITES** | |
| Rocks, bedrock stratigraphy, minerals, fossils | 3 |
| **MORPHOLOGY** | |
| Bedrock morphology, e.g., fissure valleys and morphology of Quaternary deposits | 26 |
| **PEATLANDS** | |
| Mire, fen, bog | 29 |
| **PATTERNED GROUND** | |
| Patterned ground | 7 |
| **ACCUMULATION FORMS** | |
| *Mainly formed by the inland ice* | |
| Hummocky moraine | 1 |
| Rogen moraine | 9 |
| Veiki moraine | 1 |
| Drumlins | 11 |
| End moraines | 1 |
| De Geer moraines | 4 |
| *Mainly formed by water from the melting ice-cover* | |
| Eskers, esker net | 24 |
| Delta | 19 |
| Kame | 3 |
| Sandur | 2 |

Table 3. (cont.)

| | Number |
|---|---|
| **ACCUMULATION FORMS** | |
| *Formed by the wind* | |
| Dunes | 12 |
| **EROSION FORMS IN BEDROCK** | |
| *Mainly formed by the inland ice* | |
| U-shaped valley, cirque | 9 |
| *Mainly formed by water* | |
| Canyon, kursu valley, col channel | 11 |
| Karst land | 1 |
| Cave | 3 |
| Pot-holes, etc. | 1 |
| **EROSION FORMS IN QUATERNARY DEPOSITS** | |
| *Mainly sculptured by water* | |
| Gullies | 8 |
| **ANCIENT AND RECENT SHORES** | |
| Till-capped hill, beach ridges, shingle field | 13 |
| **EROSIONAL AND DEPOSITIONAL FLUVIAL FORMS** | |
| Bluff, meander, ox-bow lake, delta | 20 |

ues for the Highest Shoreline are found in eastern Ångermanland at about 285 m a.s.l., and the largest ongoing isostatic uplift is taking place in coastal areas of southern Västerbotten, slightly more than 9 mm/year.

In the mountain areas there are, for example, ice-sculptured massive forms such as U-shaped valleys, shorelines from former ice-dammed lakes, and recent sandur plains. One of the country's best developed karst areas is found in northwestern Jämtland close to the border with Norway.

The interior is characterised by large and diversified peatlands and by moraine formations such as hummocky moraine, Rogen moraine and Veiki moraine. The glaciofluvial deltas in connection with the Highest Shoreline are found in the large river valleys.

Among objects of national interest in the coastal area, mention can be made of the De Geer moraines and the drumlin terrain in Västerbotten, till-capped hills in Ångermanland, and Sweden's largest recent delta formation in the estuary of the river Indalsälven. Sweden's northernmost raised bog is found at Nordmaling in southern Västerbotten.

# 4  CONCLUSIONS

*Olle Selinus*

In this account we have discussed and illustrated the importance of geo-science in planning our natural resources and in preserving our environment. The future for the industrial, agricultural and social infrastructure depends on the correct utilisation and management of these resources and the protection of our environment.

Bedrock, Quaternary deposits and groundwater belong to the environment that we and future generations will need for our survival. Mineral re-sources represent important raw materials for industry and for trade, fossil fuels and alternative sources of energy provide the essential energy, and groundwater is essential for our survival.

An increased population will lead to increased pressure on our natural resources and on the environment. Consequently, it is essential for us to have a detailed knowledge of how we can best make use of our resources. In this context, it is self-evident that environmental geology has an important role in community planning.

In this publication we have presented a number of individual examples of the necessity to use our basic geological knowledge. In environmental geology, SGU can contribute with the preparation of planning material and the necessary knowledge for processing and interpretation of the basic material. Examples have demonstrated that different types of basic geological material are needed in order to make the compilations and interpretations neces-

sary for these maps, adapted for decision-makers and environmental managers as well as for those of the general public who are interested in the environment.

**Environmental geology is thus an important and essential instrument in all environmental work and may result in major savings to be made in financial budgets for environmental managers, planners and decision-makers.**

## REFERENCES

**Aastrup, M., Thunholm, B., Johnson, J., Bertills, U. & Berntell, A. 1995.** Groundwater chemistry in Sweden. Environmental Protection Agency, Report No 4416. 52 p.

**Bernes, C. (ed.) 1993.** The Nordic Environment — Present state, trends and threats. Nordic council of ministers. Nord 1993:12. 211 p.

**Bernknopf, R. L., Brookshire, D. S., Soller, D. R., McKee, M. J., Sutter, J. F., Matti, J. C. & Campbell, R. H. 1993.** Societal value of Geological maps. U.S. Geological Survey Circular 1111. 53 p.

**Bertills, U. & Hanneberg, P. 1995.** Acidification in Sweden. What do we know today? Environmental Protection Agency, Report No 4422. 107 p.

**Brundin, N. H., Ek, J. I. & Selinus, O. C. 1988.** Biogeochemical studies of plants from stream banks in northern Sweden. Journal Geochemical Exploration, 27:157–188.

**Karltun, E. 1995.** Acidification of forest soils on glacial till in Sweden. Soil chemical status and acidification processes in relation to environmental conditions. Environmental Protection Agency, Report No 4427. 76 p.

**Lumsden, G. I. (ed.) 1992.** Geology and the environment in western Europe. Oxford: Clarendon press. 325 p.

**Lundgren, L. 1986.** Environmental Geology. Englewood Cliffs: Prentice-Hall. 576 p.

**McCall, J. & Marker, B. 1989.** Earth science mapping for planning, development and conservation. London: Graham and Trotman. 268 p.

**Montgomery, C. W. 1989.** Environmental geology. Dubuque: Wm. C. Brown publishers. 476 p.

**National Atlas of Sweden. 1994.** Geology. Editor C. Fredén. Stockholm: SNA förlag. 208 p.

**Naturligt surt eller antropogent försurat ytvatten i Norrland? 1995.** Slutsatser och dokumentation från en workshop i Uppsala. Naturally acid or anthropogenically acid surface water in northern Sweden. Conclusions and documentation from a workshop in Uppsala. Environmental Protection Agency, Report. 50 p.

**Nikkarinen, M, (ed.) 1996.** Geological information for environmental and land-use planning. In: Neeb, P. R. (ed.)

Geological Survey of Finland, Special Paper 22, 9–37 (this volume).

**Notter, M. (ed.) 1993.** Metals and the environment. Environmental Protection Agency of Sweden. Report 4135. 202 p.

**Pershagen, G., Axelson, O., Clavensjö, B., Damber, L., Desai, G., Enflo, A., Lagarde, F., Mellander, H., Svartengren, M., Swedjemark, G. A. & Åkerblom, G. 1993.** Radon i bostäder och lungcancer. Stockholm: Institute for Environmental Medicine, IMM Report 2/93. 42 p.

**Räisänen, M. L., Tenhola, M. & Mäkinen, J. 1992.** Relationship between mineralogy and physiochemical properties of till in Central Finland. Bulletin of the Geological Society of Finland 64 (1), 35–58.

**Ryghaug, P. 1996.** The use of digital geological information in local planning and administration. In: Neeb, P. R. (ed) Geological Survey of Finland, Special Paper 22, 39–65 (this volume).

**Selinus, O. 1983.** Regression analysis applied to interpretation of geochemical data at the Geological Survey of Sweden. In: R. J. Howarth (ed.) Handbook of exploration geochemistry, part 2, Statistics and data analysis in geochemical prospecting. Elsevier, 293–301.

**Selinus, O. S, Frank, A. & Galgan, V. 1996.** Biogeochemistry and metal biology — An integrated Swedish approach for metal related health effects. In: Appleton, D., Fuge, R. & McCall, J. (eds.) Environmental geochemistry and health with special reference to developing countries. Geological Society Special Publication 113. 264 p.

**Sveriges Geologiska Undersökning.** Berggrundskartor med beskrivning (Bedrock maps with descriptions). Series Af, Ba and Ca and Berggrundskartor (Bedrock maps) maps series Ai. Jordartskartor med beskrivning (Quaternary geology maps with descriptions). Series Ae, Ak and Ca.

**Wolff, F. 1987.** Geology for environmental planning. NGU Special publication 2. 121 p.

**Wolff, F. W., Selinus, O. C. & Tanskanen, H. 1990.** Geology for environmental planning in northern Scandinavia — a new challenge to produce small scale maps. Engineering Geology 29, 339–345.

Geological information for environmental and land-use planning
in the Mid-Norden region
Edited by Peer-Richard Neeb
Geological Survey of Finland, Special Paper 22, 105–110, 1996.

# DEFINITIONS

by
Heikki Tanskanen

| | |
|---|---|
| **Accuracy** | The closeness of observations to true values or values accepted to be true. Accuracy of geographical information has potential thematic and temporal components. |
| **Acid buffering system** | Collection of processes e.g. cation exchange, silicate weathering and carbonate dissolution, which tend to maintain the acid equilibrium of the soil. |
| **Acidification** | An increase over time of acidity (pH) and acidic compounds in e.g. soils and water. |
| **Aggregate** | In this context: any of several hard mineral materials, such as sand, gravel and crushed stone used for instance for mixing with cement or bitumen to form concrete or asphalt. |
| **Analogue** | A term used in the sense of analogue data ( e.g. on paper) in contrast to digital data. |
| **Anthropogenic** | Originating from human activity. |
| **Aqua Regia** | Abbreviation A.R. A mixture of one part nitric acid and three parts hydrochloric acid, used for dissolving minerals and metals including gold. Also called nitrohydrochloric acid. |
| **Aquifer** | A deposit of ground water. |
| **ASCII** | An American Standard Code for Information Interchange. A set of codes for representing alphanumeric information (often referred to flat - file or text - file). |
| **Attributes** | 1) A characteristic of a geographic feature described by numbers or characters, typically stored in tabular format, and linked to the feature by a user-assigned identifier. 2) Non-graphic information associated with point, line or area element. |
| **Base cations** | A group of exchangeable elements usually consisting of $Ca^{2+}$, $Mg^{2+}$, $K^+$ and $Na^+$. |
| **Bioavailable** | An element or chemical compound in a form in which it can be assimilated by organisms, i.e. a nutrient available for living organisms. |
| **Buffer capacity** | The capacity of a substance to resist changes in pH. |

**Buffering techniques**    Delimiting zones of specific distance around a feature (in GIS). The resulting buffer zones form polygons — areas that are either inside or outside the specified buffer distance from each feature.

**Catchment area**    The area of land bounded by watersheds draining into a river, basin or reservoir. Also called catchment basin, drainage area or drainage basin.

**Code**    A set of specific numbers or characters for representing a theme and separate attributes.

**Completeness**    The difference between an actual dataset and its specifications.

**Contamination**    A situation in which substances are present in the media (often soil or water) in such concentrations that functional properties of the soil or water for human beings, plants or animals are diminished or threatened.

**Coverage**    A digital version of a map forming the basic unit of vector data storage in the geographic information system Arc/Info.

**Cursor**    A visible symbol guided by the keyboard or a mouse, usually in the form of a cross or a blinking symbol, that indicates a position (location) on a computer screen.

**Dataset**    An identifiable collection of data.

**Datum**    A set of parameters and control points used to accurately define the three-dimensional shape of the Earth (e.g., as a spheroide). The corresponding datum is the basis for the planar coordinate system. For example, ED50 (the European datum from 1950) is one of the datums for the UTM map projection and coordinates.

**DeGeer moraine**    A small moraine ridge usually a couple of hundred meters long and up to 5 m high. Occurs in swarms and is considered to be formed in the marginal zone of the inland ice, in cracks running parallel to the ice margin.

**Delta**    An alluvial (transported and deposited by running water) deposit in water at the outflow of a river.

**Deposit**    The term mineral deposit or sand and gravel deposit is used to designate a natural occurrence of a useful mineral or a building material of possible economic interest.

**Digital**    Representing data as a series of numerical values.

**Digital geological information**    Geological information in numeric form.

**Dimension stone**    Stone that is quarried or cut in accordance with required dimensions, and used as building material.

**Drumlin**    A low smoothly rounded elongate oval ridge, mostly consisting of till and aligned parallel to the direction of the movement of the inland ice.

**Eluvial layer**    The topsoil horizon from which materials have been removed by either mechanical or chemical means.

**Environmental geology**    The science concerning the interaction between human activity, the geological environment and nature.

**Environmental hazard**    A present or potential danger due to some state or property that produces a substantial risk to human life or to the environment.

**Environmental risk**    A present or potential chance that substantial hazard will occur in environment.

| | |
|---|---|
| **Erosion** | The process whereby the materials of the Earth's crust are loosened, dissolved, or worn away, and simultaneously moved from place to another, by natural agencies, which include weathering, solution, corrasion, and transportation. The mechanical destruction of the land and the removal of material by running water, waves, moving ice or wind. |
| **Esker** | A long, narrow, sharp ridge of glaciofluvial drift, deposited by a stream in a subglacial tunnel. |
| **Extent** | The horizontal and vertical geographic space and time period covered by a dataset. |
| **Feature** | 1) The type of feature represented in a coverage (arcs, labels, points, polygons, annotations, boundaries etc.) <br> 2) The type of representation for a map feature, often called an object, an entity or a geographic phenomen. |
| **Fines** | In this context: minerogenic soil fraction < 0.06 mm in diameter. |
| **Gamma radiation** | Electromagnetic radiation emitted as the result of a nuclear process. |
| **Geochemistry** | The study of the distribution and amounts of the chemical elements and their isotopes in minerals, ores, rocks, soils, water, and the atmosphere, as well as circulation of the elements in nature. |
| **Geographic Area** | The spatial coverage of a dataset defined according to an indirect spatial reference system, such as a county or a municipality. |
| **Geographical dataset** | A structured collection of geographic data. |
| **Geographical information** | Information concerning phenomena directly or indirectly associated with a location relative to the surface of the Earth. |
| **Geographical Information System (GIS)** | A set of computer programs or a system for capturing, storing, checking, manipulating, analysing, transforming and displaying data or information which is spatially referenced to the Earth. |
| **Glacial** | In geology, pertaining to, characteristic of, produced or deposited by, or derived from a glacier. |
| **Glaciofluvial** | Pertaining to melt-water flowing from melting glacier ice. |
| **GPS** | Global Position System. Satellite based navigation system. |
| **Groundwater** | The subsurface water occurring in the saturated zone. |
| **Gyttja** | A dark, pulpy, freshwater mud characterized by abundant organic matter that is more or less determinable, and deposited or precipitated in a march or in a lake whose waters are rich in nutrients and oxygen. |
| **Heavy metals** | A diverse group of metals, metalloids and other elements. The term includes essential trace nutrients e.g. Cu, Zn and Se, non-essential nutrients as Ni and toxic metals e.g. Pb, Hg and Cd. For istance most sulphide-forming elements with a relatively high specific gravity ( > 4.5 g/cm$^3$). |
| **Hot link** | A facility in ArcView that allows one to access virtually any other data source or application, simply by clicking on a map feature. |
| **Hummocky moraine** | Moraine formation composed of hummocks and hollows. |
| **Humus** | Layer of partly decomposed raw plant and animal residues that lies below the litter in a podzol profile. |
| **ICP** | Inductively Coupled Plasma Spectrometry. Analytical method. |
| **Illuvial horizon** | Soil horizon into which material has been concentrated chemically — precipitation of Fe, Al and Si. |

| | |
|---|---|
| **Infiltration capacity** | 1) In hydrology penetrating of water from the soil surface into the soil. 2) The suitability of a superficial deposit to receive and clean seawage or effluent, mainly based on the permeability or hydraulic conductivity of the deposit. |
| **Infiltration map** | A derivative map based on the infiltration properties of surficial deposits. |
| **Kame** | A mound or hummock with marked sides or on irregular ridge, mainly consisting of glaciofluvial sediments deposited in contact with a glacier or the inland ice. |
| **Lithology** | Description of rocks. Physical characteristics of a rock, including colour, composition and texture. |
| **Littoral** | Formed on the shore zone of a lake or the sea. |
| **Look-up table** | An array of data values that can be quickly accessed by a computer to convert data from one form to another, e.g. from attribute values to colours. |
| **Map scale** | The extent of reduction needed to display a representation of the Earth's surface on a map. |
| **Marginal moraine** | A ridge composed of till and glaciofluvial material and deposited at the ice margin. |
| **Marine deposits** | Fine-grained sediments originally deposited on the sea floor. |
| **Medical geology** | The science concerning the impact of geology (and other aspects) on human and animal health. |
| **Medium** | In this context: an expression of what environmental position the object is situated (in the air, beneath the water surface, beneath the ground surface etc.). |
| **Metadata** | Data describing the content of the data and the business aspects of it (representation, extent, spatial reference, quality and administration). |
| **Metamorphism** | Process by which consolidated rocks are altered in composition, texture or internal structure by increased pressure and heat. It generally includes the development of new minerals. |
| **Morphology** | The form and structure of objects or deposits, a term often used in different branches of natural science. |
| **Mouse** | In this context: a hand-controlled hardware device for interacting with a computer terminal or entering data from a digitizer. |
| **Natural radioactivity** | The property of bedrock or mineral shown by some elements of changing into other elements, by the emission of charged particles from their nuclei. In geology, usually measured as gamma rays by a scintillometer. |
| **Network** | 1) Two or more interconnected computer systems. 2) A set of interconnected lines (roads, etc.). |
| **Nutrient** | A chemical element that is considered essential for life and growth. |
| **Object** | 1) The type of representation for a map object, usually called a feature. 2) An entity or a geographic phenomen. 3) A geological matter. |
| **Overlay** | The process of stacking digital representations of various spatial data on top of each other so that each position in the area covered can be analysed in terms of these data. |
| **Partial master plan** | A general plan for land use in an certain area. |

| | |
|---|---|
| **Patterned ground** | Well-defined symmetrical forms, such as circles, polygons, nets etc. that are characterised of, but not necessarily confined to, surficial material subject to intensive frost action. |
| **Permeability** | Ability of soil to transmit fluids under pressure. |
| **Petrophysics** | Study of the physical properties of rocks. |
| **pH** | A measure of the acidity of a substance, defined as the negative log10 of the hydrogen ion activity. |
| **Pixel** | The smallest part of coded (often coloured or rastered) picture image. |
| **Podzol** | Soil type common in coniferous forests in northern countries. Characterized by distinct horizons of eluviation (leaching) and illuviation (enrichment) in vertical sections of soil. |
| **Polygon** | In this context: a multisided figure that represents an area on the map. |
| **Positional accuracy** | A primary parameter indicating accuracy of geographic position within a geographic dataset or subset. |
| **Quality parameters** | A quantitative indicator of quality of a geographic dataset. |
| **Quality** | The degree of fitness for use of a geographic dataset or subset for stated or implied needs, defined by indicators such as lineage, usage and quality parameters. |
| **Quarry** | An open pit or surface working, usually for the extraction of ores, industrial minerals or dimension stone. |
| **Quaternary** | The latest period of geologic time, the time of extensive glaciations in northern Europe and in North America (the last 2.4 million years). |
| **Quaternary map** | Map showing the distribution of surficial deposits deposited during the Quaternary period of the Earth's history (the last 2.4 million years, and in northern countries mainly during the last deglaciation which started 15,000 to 18,000 years ago). |
| **Query** | Execution of a statement to retrieve selected information from a source. |
| **Radiometric** | The measurement of ionizing radiation. |
| **Raster** | A cellular data structure composed of rows and columns. Groups of cells represent features. |
| **Retention capacity** | The ability of soil to retain liquid substances. |
| **Rogen moraine** | Hilly moraine landscape characterized by more or less regular ridges that are mainly oriented perpendicular to the ice movement direction. |
| **Saturated zone** | That part of the lithosphere where the soil pores are completely filled with water. |
| **Solid geology** | Gives information on the composition of the Earth's crust under a layer of overburden. |
| **SOSI** | This stands for "Samordnet Opplegg for Stedfestet Informasjon" in Norwegian or Coordinated System for Geographic Information. It deals with the techniques and data definitions of geographical information, and is *de facto* Norwegian standardized description of geometry, topology, quality, positioning systems and thematic coding. |
| **Su(pe)rficial deposits** | The material (clay, silt, sand, gravel, stones) consisting of unconsolidated residual, alluvial, or glacial deposits lying on top of the bedrock. In Nordic countries deposited during the Quaternary period. |

| | |
|---|---|
| **Sustainable development** | Development that meets the needs of the present without compromising the ability of future generations to meet their own needs. |
| **Terminal moraine** | A large end moraine composed of till and/or glaciofluvial material that has formed as the result of the ice margin remaining stationary. |
| **Thematic accuracy** | A primary quality parameter indicating the accuracy of thematic attributes of a geographic dataset or subset. |
| **Till** | Material deposited by glaciers or inland ice. Till has a varying composition of boulders, stones, gravel, sand, fine sand, silt and clay. |
| **Topology** | The spatial relationships between connecting or adjacent coverage features (e.g. lines, polygons, points in GIS). |
| **Transfer** | Movement of a dataset from one computer (or GIS-program) to another. |
| **U-valley** | Valley with the shape of an U in section, formed through glacial erosion. |
| **Update date** | Date stamp applied to the updated feature to indicate the date at which the update was applied. |
| **Vector** | A coordinate-based data structure commonly used to represent linear map features. |
| **Veiki moraine** | Moraine hills similar to plateaus with numerous circular bodies of water. |
| **Weathering** | Physical and chemical changes produced in rocks, often at or near the surface, by atmospheric agents, which results in more or less complete disintegration and decomposition. |
| **XRF** | X-ray fluorescence. Analytical method for determining the total contents of elements. |
| **Zoom** | Used in the sense of displaying a region smaller than the full extent of the spatial data set, enlarging it and showing greater detail. |